INTERNATIONAL SERIES OF MONOGRAPHS ON

PURE AND APPLIED MATHEMATICS

VOLUME 24

OPERATIONAL CALCULUS IN TWO VARIABLES

and its applications

OTHER TITLES IN THE SERIES
ON PURE AND APPLIED MATHEMATICS

Vol. 1. WALLACE—*Introduction to Algebraic Topology*
Vol. 2. PEDOE—*Circles*
Vol. 3. SPAIN—*Analytical Conics*
Vol. 4. MIKHLIN—*Integral Equations*
Vol. 5. EGGLESTON—*Problems in Euclidean Space: Application of Convexity*
Vol. 6. WALLACE—*Homology Theory on Algebraic Varieties*
Vol. 7. NOBLE—*Methods Based on the Wiener-Hopf Technique for the Solution of Partial Differential Equations*
Vol. 8. MIKUSINSKI—*Operational Calculus*
Vol. 9. HEINE—*Group Theory in Quantum Mechanics*
Vol. 10. BLAND—*The Theory of Linear Viscoelasticity*
Vol. 11. KURTH—*Axiomatics of Classical Statistical Mathematics*
Vol. 12. FUCHS—*Abelian Groups*
Vol. 13. KURATOWSKI—*Introduction to Set Theory and Topology*
Vol. 14. SPAIN—*Analytical Quadrics*
Vol. 15. HARTMAN and MIKUSINSKI—*Theory of Measure and Lebesgue Integration*
Vol. 16. KULCZYCKI—*Non-Euclidean Geometry*
Vol. 17. KURATOWSKI—*Introduction to Calculus*
Vol. 18. GERONIMUS—*Polynomials Orthogonal on a Circle and Interval*
Vol. 19. ELSGOLC—*Calculus of Variations*
Vol. 20. ALEXITS—*Convergence Problems of Orthogonal Series*
Vol. 21. FUCHS and LEVIN—*Functions of a Complex Variable: Vol. II*
Vol. 22. GOODSTEIN—*Fundamental Concepts of Mathematics*
Vol. 23. KEENE—*Abstract Sets and Finite Ordinals*

PUBLISHER'S NOTICE
TO REVIEWERS AND READERS

CONCERNING THE QUALITY OF PRODUCTION AND PUBLISHED PRICE OF THIS WORK

In the interest of speedily making available the information contained in this publication, it has been necessary to produce the text by non-letterpress setting and photo lithography, with the result that the quality of production is not as high as the public have come to associate with and expect from the Pergamon Press.

To have re-set this manuscript by letterpress would have delayed its appearance by many months and the price would have had to be increased further.

The cost of translating scientific and technical works from the Russian in time, money, and publishing effort is very considerable. In the interest of getting the Soviet Authorities eventually to pay the usual authors' royalties to Western authors, the Pergamon Press is voluntarily paying to Russian authors the usual authors' royalties on this publication, in addition to the translators' and editors' fees. This and the somewhat limited market and the lack of any kind of subsidy accounts for what may appear to be a higher than usual published price.

I. R. MAXWELL
Publisher at Pergamon Press

В. А. Диткин и А. П. Прудников

ОПЕРАЦИОННОЕ ИСЧИСЛЕНИЕ ПО ДВУМ ПЕРЕМЕННЫМ И ЕГО ПРИЛОЖЕНИЯ

OPERATIONAL CALCULUS IN TWO VARIABLES AND ITS APPLICATIONS

By

V. A. DITKIN and A. P. PRUDNIKOV

Translated by

D. M. G. WISHART

Lecturer in Statistics,
The University of Birmingham

PERGAMON PRESS

NEW YORK · OXFORD · LONDON · PARIS

1962

PERGAMON PRESS INC.
122 East 55th Street, New York 22, N.Y.
1404 New York Avenue N.W., Washington 5 D.C.

PERGAMON PRESS LTD.
Headington Hill Hall, Oxford
4 & 5 Fitzroy Square, London W.1

PERGAMON PRESS S.A.R.L.
24 Rue des Écoles, Paris Ve

PERGAMON PRESS G.m.b.H.
Kaiserstrasse 75, Frankfurt am Main

A translation of the original volume
Operatsionnoye ischisleniye po dvum peremennym i ego prilozheniya
(Fizmatgiz, Moscow, 1958)

Library of Congress Card Number: 62-9177

Printed in Great Britain by Compton Printing Works, London

TABLE OF CONTENTS

PART ONE

Fundamental Theory

PART TWO

Tables of Formulae

PREFACE

This book contains an account of the operational calculus in two variables based on the two-dimensional Laplace transform. It is well known that the operational calculus has obtained a wide circulation in different fields of scientific investigation, and a large number of works has been published on the theory and application of operational calculus for functions of one variable in the Russian and other literature. But monographs on the operational calculus in two variables have been rare in the literature, although a considerable number of papers has been devoted to this question in recent years, and the authors felt that it was necessary to attempt to set down the fundamental results of this subject.

Because of the great practical significance of the operational calculus the authors have tended to quote a full and varied list of operational formulae. In several cases they have consciously allowed a lapse of rigour in their account in giving much attention to the technique of the calculations. This is justified in the end, since in the majority of cases the restrictions necessary for the validity of the final formulae are frequently weaker than those required for legitimacy of all the intermediate steps.

A knowledge of the operational calculus in one variable is required for the study of this book [1-4]*.

In compiling this monograph the literature has been consulted at the sources, a list of which is included at the end of the book. From this list we would particularly mention Voelker, D. and Doetsch, G., Die Zweidimensionale Laplace-Transformation, Basel (1950); and Poli, L. and Delerue, P., Le calcul symbolique à deux variables et ses applications. Mémorial des Sciences Mathématiques, fasc. 127, Paris (1954).

We express our thanks to M.V.Yakovin for his careful editing of the manuscript and for a number of valuable suggestions.

The authors realize that this work is not without a number of deficiencies and they will be very grateful to all readers sending their remarks to: Moscow, Lenin Prospect, d.15, Fizmatgiz, Editor, Mathematical Literature.

TRANSLATOR'S NOTE

The notations used in this book are those of Continental Europe, and the reader accustomed to the Anglo-American usage should consult the List of Notations in Part II whenever he is in doubt about the exact meaning of a symbol.

The Translator.

PART ONE

Fundamental Theory

CHAPTER 1

THE TWO-DIMENSIONAL LAPLACE TRANSFORM

The well-known integral transform of Laplace was apparently considered for the first time in 1812 [40]. Since then many papers have been devoted to the study of the properties of this transform and its numerous applications, and the idea naturally arose of generalizing the transform to functions of two variables. During the 1930s short notes [33, 34, 35] on the operational calculus in two variables based on the two-dimensional Laplace transform appeared. In the works of Delerue [19] and Doetsch [22] the methods of the operational calculus in several variables were successfully applied to the solution of differential equations by the study of the properties of special functions etc. Indian mathematicians have contributed several papers on this same theme [10, 11, 55]. In recent times Soviet physicists have applied the operational methods of A.V.Lykov to the analytic investigation of processes of heat and mass transfer [4, 5].

We discuss the fundamental properties of the two-dimensional Laplace transform as the basis of an operational calculus in two variables.

1. The Laplace Integral

We suppose that $f(x, y)$ is a real or complex valued function of two real variables, defined on the region $R(0 \leqslant x < \infty,\ 0 \leqslant y < \infty)$ and integrable in the sense of Lebesgue over an arbitrary finite rectangle $R_{a,b}(0 \leqslant x \leqslant a,\ 0 \leqslant y \leqslant b)$.

We shall consider the expression

$$F(p, q; a, b) = \int_0^a \int_0^b e^{-px-qy} f(x, y)\, dx\, dy, \qquad (1.1)$$

where $p = \sigma + i\mu$ and $q = \tau + i\nu$ are complex parameters determining a point (p, q) in the plane of two complex dimensions. Let S be the class of all functions $f(x, y)$, such that the following conditions are satisfied for at least one point (p, q):

1. The integral (1.1) is bounded at the point (p, q) with respect to the variables a and b; i.e.,

$$|F(p, q; \; a, b)| < M(p, q)$$

for all $a \geqslant 0$, $b \geqslant 0$, where $M(p, q)$ is a positive constant independent of a and b.

2. At the point (p, q)

$$\lim_{\substack{a \to \infty \\ b \to \infty}} F(p, q; \; a, b) = F(p, q).$$

exists. We denote this limit by

$$F(p, q) = L_{p, q}\{f(x, y)\} = \int_0^\infty \int_0^\infty e^{-px-qy} f(x, y)\, dx\, dy. \quad (1.2),$$

The integral (1.2) is called the two-dimensional Laplace transform (or integral) of the function $f(x, y)$.

If the conditions 1 and 2 are satisfied simultaneously, we will say that the integral (1.2) converges boundedly in at least one point (p, q). Thus the class S consists of functions for which the integral (1.2) converges boundedly for at least one point (p, q). When the integral (1.2) converges boundedly, we will call $f(x, y)$ the determining function and $F(p, q)$ the generating function. *

Remark 1. If the function $f(x, y)$ satisfies the condition

$$|f(x, y)| \leqslant Me^{hx + ky} \quad (1.3)$$

for all $x \geqslant 0$, $y \geqslant 0$ (where M, h, k are positive constants), then it is not difficult to verify that $f(x, y)$ belongs to the class S at all points (p, q) for which $\operatorname{Re} p > h$, $\operatorname{Re} q > k$.

Remark 2. If the function $f(x, y) = f_1(x) f_2(y)$ and the integrals

$$F_1(p) = \int_0^\infty e^{-px} f_1(x)\, dx, \quad F_2(q) = \int_0^\infty e^{-qy} f_2(y)\, dy$$

exist then $f(x, y)$ belongs to the class S and $F(p, q) = F_1(p) F_2(q)$.

* The nomenclature is that of Widder, The Laplace Transform, Princeton (1941).

Theorem 1. If the integral (1.2) converges boundedly at the point (p_0, q_0), then it converges boundedly at all points (p, q) for which $\mathrm{Re}\,(p - p_0) > 0$, $\mathrm{Re}\,(q - q_0) > 0$.

Proof. Integrating by parts we obtain:

$$F(p, q;\, a, b) = \int_0^a e^{-px}\,dx \int_0^b e^{-(q-q_0)\,y} d_y \int_0^y f(x, y)\, e^{-q_0\eta} d\eta =$$

$$= \int_0^a e^{-px}\,dx \left\{ e^{-(q-q_0)\,b} \int_0^b e^{-q_0\eta} f(x, \eta)\, d\eta + \right.$$

$$\left. + (q - q_0) \int_0^b e^{-(q-q_0)\,y}\,dy \int_0^y e^{-q_0\eta} f(x, \eta)\, d\eta \right\} =$$

$$= \int_0^a e^{-(p-p_0)\,x}\, d_x \int_0^x e^{-p_0\xi}\,d\xi \left\{ e^{-(q-q_0)\,b} \int_0^b e^{-q_0\eta} f(\xi, \eta)\, d\eta + \right.$$

$$\left. + (q - q_0) \int_0^b e^{-(q-q_0)\,y}\,dy \int_0^y e^{-q_0\eta} f(\xi, \eta)\, d\eta \right\} =$$

$$= e^{-(p-p_0)\,a} \int_0^a e^{-p_0\xi}\,d\xi \left\{ e^{-(q-q_0)\,b} \int_0^b e^{-q_0\eta} f(\xi, \eta)\, d\eta + \right.$$

$$\left. + (q - q_0) \int_0^b e^{-(q-q_0)\,y}\,dy \int_0^y e^{-q_0\eta} f(\xi, \eta)\, d\eta \right\} +$$

$$+ (p - p_0) \int_0^a e^{-(p-p_0)\,x}\,dx \int_0^x e^{-p_0\xi}\,d\xi \left\{ e^{-(q-q_0)\,b} \int_0^b e^{-q_0\eta} \times \right.$$

$$\left. \times f(\xi, \eta)\, d\eta + (q - q_0) \int_0^b e^{-(q-q_0)\,y}\,dy \int_0^y e^{-q_0\eta} f(\xi, \eta)\, d\eta \right\} =$$

$$= e^{-(p-p_0)\,a - (q-q_0)\,b} \int_0^a \int_0^b e^{-p_0\xi - q_0\eta} f(\xi, \eta)\, d\xi\, d\eta +$$

$$+ (p - p_0)\, e^{-(q-q_0)\,b} \int_0^a e^{-(p-p_0)\,x}\,dx \int_0^x e^{-p_0\xi}\,d\xi \times$$

$$\times \int_0^b e^{-q_0\eta} f(\xi, \eta)\, d\eta + (q - q_0)\, e^{-(p-p_0)\,a} \int_0^b e^{-(q-q_0)\,y}\,dy \times$$

$$\times \int_0^a e^{-p_0\xi}\, d\xi \int_0^y e^{-q_0\eta} f(\xi, \eta)\, d\eta +$$

$$+ (p - p_0)(q - q_0) \int_0^a e^{-(p-p_0)x}\, dx \int_0^b e^{-(q-q_0)y}\, dy \times$$

$$\times \int_0^x e^{-p_0\xi}\, d\xi \int_0^y e^{-q_0\eta} f(\xi, \eta)\, d\eta.$$

Writing

$$\varphi(x, y) = \int_0^x e^{-p_0\xi}\, d\xi \int_0^y e^{-q_0\eta} f(\xi, \eta)\, d\eta,$$

this becomes

$$\begin{aligned} F(p, q;\, a, b) &= e^{-(p-p_0)a-(q-q_0)b}\varphi(a, b) + \\ &+ (p - p_0)\, e^{-(q-q_0)b} \int_0^a e^{-(p-p_0)x}\varphi(x, b)\, dx + \\ &+ (q - q_0)\, e^{-(p-p_0)a} \int_0^b e^{-(q-q_0)y}\varphi(a, y)\, dy + \\ &+ (p - p_0)(q - q_0) \int_0^a e^{-(p-p_0)x}\, dx \int_0^b e^{-(q-q_0)y}\, \varphi(x, y)\, dy. \end{aligned} \tag{1.4}$$

If we define h and k by $\operatorname{Re}(p - p_0) = h$, $\operatorname{Re}(q - q_0) = k$ and take into account that

$$|\varphi(x, y)| < M(p_0, q_0) = M, \tag{1.5}$$

then

$$\begin{aligned} |F(p, q;\, a, b)| &\leqslant e^{-ha-kb}M + \\ &+ |p - p_0|\, e^{-kb} \int_0^a Me^{-hx}\, dx + |q - q_0|\, e^{-pa} \int_0^b Me^{-ky}\, dy + \\ &+ |p - p_0|\,|q - q_0| \int_0^a \int_0^b Me^{-hx-ky}\, dx\, dy. \end{aligned}$$

If $h > 0$, $k > 0$, we have

$$|F(p, q; a, b)| \leqslant$$
$$\leqslant M\left(1+\frac{|p-p_0|}{h}+\frac{|q-q_0|}{k}+\frac{|p-p_0||q-q_0|}{hk}\right), \quad (1.6)$$

so that condition 1 is satisfied. Because the function $\varphi(x, y)$ is bounded, the existence of $\lim\limits_{\substack{a\to\infty \\ b\to\infty}} F(p, q; a, b)$ follows from (1.4) and

$$\lim_{\substack{a\to\infty \\ b\to\infty}} F(p, q; a, b)=$$
$$=(p-p_0)(q-q_0)\int_0^\infty\int_0^\infty e^{-(p-p_0)x-(q-q_0)y}\varphi(x, y)\,dx\,dy, \quad (1.7)$$

from which it follows that condition 2 is satisfied and the theorem is proved.

The simultaneous fulfilment of conditions 1 and 2 is essential. We shall show by means of an example that if condition 2 is satisfied at some point (p_0, q_0) but condition 1 is not satisfied, Theorem 1 may no longer be valid.

In fact, let us consider

$$f(x, y)=\begin{cases} 0 & \text{for } 0\leqslant x\leqslant 2,\ 0\leqslant y\leqslant 2 \text{ and for } x\geqslant 2,\ y\geqslant 2; \\ e^{x^2} & \text{for } 2<x<\infty,\ 0\leqslant y<1; \\ -e^{x^2} & \text{for } 2<x<\infty,\ 1\leqslant y<2; \\ e^{y^2} & \text{for } 0\leqslant x<1,\ 2<y<\infty; \\ -e^{y^2} & \text{for } 1\leqslant x<2,\ 2<y<\infty. \end{cases}$$

For $a \geqslant 2$ and $b \geqslant 2$, we have

$$\int_0^a\int_0^b f(x, y)\,dx\,dy=0$$

and

$$\lim_{\substack{a\to\infty \\ b\to\infty}}\int_0^a\int_0^b f(x, y)\,dx\,dy=0,$$

so that $F(0, 0)=0$. On the other hand, for $a \geqslant 2$ and $b \geqslant 2$ we have

$$F(p,\ q;\ a,\ b) = \int_2^a e^{-px}\,dx\left[e^{x^2}\int_0^1 e^{-qy}\,dy - e^{x^2}\int_1^2 e^{-qy}\,dy\right] +$$

$$+\int_2^b e^{-qy}\,dy\left[e^{y^2}\int_0^1 e^{-px}\,dx - e^{y^2}\int_1^2 e^{-px}\,dx\right] =$$

$$= \frac{1}{q}(1-e^{-q})^2\int_2^a e^{-px+x^2}\,dx + \frac{1}{p}(1-e^{-p})^2\int_2^b e^{-qy+y^2}\,dy,$$

from which it follows that if p and q are not simultaneously equal to zero the limit $\lim\limits_{\substack{a\to\infty\\ b\to\infty}} F(p,\ q;\ a,\ b)$ does not exist.

2. The Region of Convergence

We shall denote by D the set of all points $(p,\ q)$, for which the integral (1.2) is boundedly convergent, and we shall call this the region of convergence of the Laplace integral. We remark here that the convergence or divergence of the integral (1.2) for all real values $(p,\ q)$ implies the convergence or divergence for all complex values $(p,\ q)$

Let now$(p,\ q)$ be real numbers, and let $J(p_0,\ q_0)$ be the open set consisting of all real points for which $p > p_0$ $q > q_0$. We shall assume that there exist points $(p,\ q)$ where the integral (1.2) converges and points where it diverges. In the real pq-plane we consider the collection of lines.

$$q = p + \lambda \quad (-\infty < \lambda + \infty),$$

where λ is a real number. We choose one of these lines corresponding to a value $\lambda = \lambda_0$ (see Fig. 1), and we locate on this line the points where the integral (1.2) converges and the points where it diverges. If the integral converges at some point $(p,\ p+\lambda_0)$ then, according to Theorem 1, it converges at all points of the open region $J(p,\ p+\lambda_0)$.

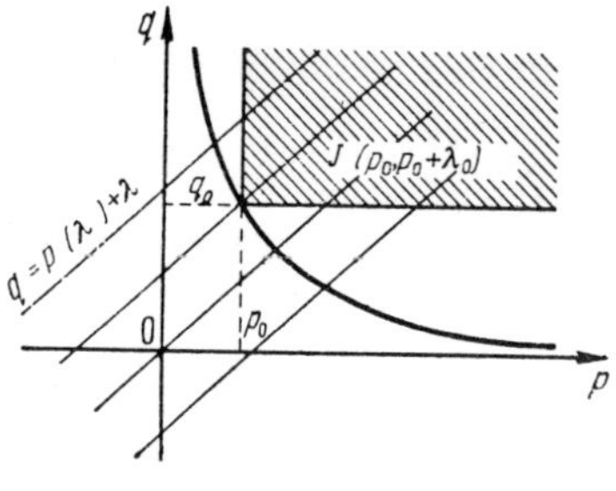

Fig. 1

Consequently, we deduce from this that for each value $\lambda = \lambda_0$ there exists a finite number $p_0 = p(\lambda_0)$ such that the integral (1.2) converges for all $p > p_0$ $q = p + \lambda_0$ and diverges for $p < p_0$, $q = p + \lambda_0$ By varying λ, we obtain a set of points (a) in the (real) pq -plane defined by the parametric equations

$$\left.\begin{aligned} p &= p(\lambda) \\ q &= p(\lambda) + \lambda \end{aligned}\right\} (-\infty < \lambda < \infty).$$

$p(\lambda)$ is a non-increasing function so that the limit $p(\lambda + 0)$ exists and is finite, and $p(\lambda + 0) \leqslant p(\lambda)$. The inequality $p(\lambda + 0) < p(\lambda)$, however, is impossible since in that case we could determine a number $\delta > 0$, such that the point $[p(\lambda),\ p(\lambda) + \lambda]$ is inside the region $J[p(\lambda + \delta),\ p(\lambda + \delta) + \lambda + \delta]$, and this contradicts the definition of $p(\lambda)$ Hence, $p(\lambda + 0) = p(\lambda)$, and by analogous reasoning we can show also that $p(\lambda - 0) = p(\lambda)$.

Thus, the set of points (a) is a continuous non-increasing curve which separates the pq-plane into two open sets, D_1, defined by the conditions

$$\left.\begin{aligned} p &> p(\lambda) \\ q &= p(\lambda) + \lambda \end{aligned}\right\} (-\infty < \lambda < \infty),$$

where the integral (1.2) converges, and D_2, defined by

$$\left.\begin{aligned} p &< p(\lambda) \\ q &= p(\lambda) + \lambda \end{aligned}\right\} (-\infty < \lambda < \infty).$$

where it diverges. At points on the curve the integral can have either property. We shall call this non-increasing continuous curve (a) the characteristic of convergence of the Laplace integral (1.2).

Passing to complex values of q and q, we define the set D of points $(p,\ q)$, for which (Re p, Re q) belongs to the region D_1. When the integral (1.2) converges on the characteristic of convergence, points whose real parts (Re p, Re q) lie on this characteristic are also included in the set D.

We have thus the following possibilities:

1. The integral (1.2) converges in the entire real plane.
2. The integral converges nowhere.
3. There exists some region of convergence, open or closed, inside which the integral (1.2) converges, and outside which it diverges.

We remark that if the points $(p_1,\ q_1)$ and $(p_2,\ q_2)$ belong to the region of convergence and $\operatorname{Re} p_1 < \operatorname{Re} p_2$, $\operatorname{Re} q_1 < \operatorname{Re} q_2$ then, according to Theorem 1, all points $(p,\ q)$ satisfying $\operatorname{Re} p_1 < \operatorname{Re} p <$

$< \operatorname{Re} p_2$, and $\operatorname{Re} q_1 < \operatorname{Re} q < \operatorname{Re} q_2$ also belong to the region of convergence.

Example 1. If $f(x, y) = e^{\alpha x + \beta y}$ (α, β real numbers), then

$$\int_0^\infty \int_0^\infty e^{-px-qy} e^{\alpha x + \beta y}\, dx\, dy = \frac{1}{(p-\alpha)(q-\beta)}.$$

The region of convergence is shown in Fig.2.

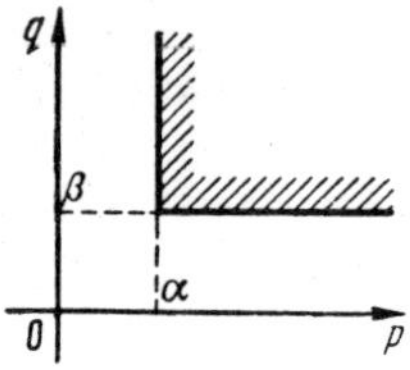

Fig. 2

Example 2. If
$$f(x, y) = \begin{cases} e^x & \text{for} \quad x \leqslant y, \\ e^y & \text{for} \quad x > y, \end{cases}$$
then

$$\int_0^\infty \int_0^\infty e^{-px-qy} f(x, y)\, dx\, dy = \frac{p+q}{pq(p+q-1)}.$$

The region of convergence is shown in Fig.3.

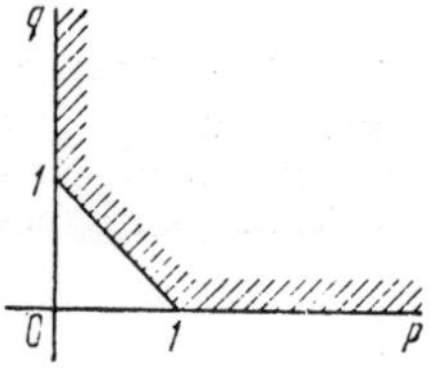

Fig. 3

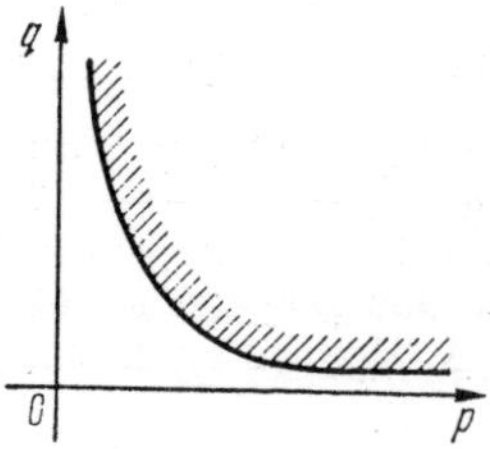

Fig. 4

Example 3. If $f(x, y) = I_0(2\sqrt{xy})$, then

$$\int_0^\infty \int_0^\infty e^{-px-qy} I_0(2\sqrt{xy})\, dx\, dy = \frac{1}{pq-1}.$$

The region of convergence is shown in Fig.4.

3. Uniformly Bounded Convergence

Definition. Δ is a set of points (p, q). We shall say that the convergence of the integral (1.2) is uniformly bounded on the set Δ if the following conditions are satisfied:

1. There exists a positive constant M, independent of a and b and all (p, q) in the set Δ, such that the integral (1.1) satisfies

$$|F(p, q; a, b)| < M,$$

2. The limit

$$\lim_{\substack{a \to \infty \\ b \to \infty}} F(p, q; a, b) = F(p, q)$$

exists, and the convergence is uniform with respect to all (p, q) belonging to Δ, i.e. given $\varepsilon > 0$, we can find numbers $A(\varepsilon)$ and $B(\varepsilon)$, such that

$$|F(p, q) - F(p, q; a, b)| < \varepsilon$$

for $a \geqslant A(\varepsilon)$, $b \geqslant B(\varepsilon)$ and all (p, q) in the set Δ.

Theorem 2. If the integral (1.2) converges boundedly at the point (p_0, q_0), then

1) the integral (1.1) is bounded uniformly with respect to all (p, q) belonging to the region Δ_0 defined by the inequalities:

$$\operatorname{Re}(p - p_0) > |p - p_0| \cos\theta, \quad \operatorname{Re}(q - q_0) > |q - q_0| \cos\theta$$
$$\left(0 \leqslant \theta < \frac{\pi}{2}\right);$$

2) the convergence of the integral (1.2) is uniformly bounded on a set Δ_1 defined by the inequalities:

$$\operatorname{Re}(p - p_0) \geqslant \bar{\delta} > 0, \quad \operatorname{Re}(q - q_0) \geqslant \delta > 0,$$
$$\operatorname{Re}(p - p_0) \geqslant |p - p_0| \cos\theta, \quad \operatorname{Re}(q - q_0) \geqslant |q - q_0| \cos\theta,$$

where $\delta > 0$ and $\theta \left(0 < \theta < \frac{\pi}{2}\right)$ are arbitrary real numbers.

Proof. 1. From the inequality (1.6) we deduce that

$$|F(p, q; a, b)| \leqslant M \left(1 + \frac{1}{\cos\theta}\right)^2$$

for all $a \geqslant 0$, $b \geqslant 0$ and all (p, q) in Δ_0.

2. According to (1.4), (1.5), and (1.7) we have

$$|F(p, q) - F(p, q; a, b)| =$$

$$= \Big| (p-p_0)(q-q_0) \int_0^\infty \int_0^\infty e^{-(p-p_0)x-(q-q_0)y} \varphi(x, y)\, dx\, dy -$$

$$- e^{-(p-p_0)a-(q-q_0)b} \varphi(a, b) - (p-p_0) e^{-(q-q_0)b} \int_0^a e^{-(p-p_0)x} \times$$

$$\times \varphi(x, b)\, dx - (q-q_0) e^{-(p-p_0)a} \int_0^b e^{-(q-q_0)y} \varphi(a, y)\, dy -$$

$$-(p-p_0)(q-q_0) \int_0^a e^{-(p-p_0)x}\, dx \int_0^b e^{-(q-q_0)y} \varphi(x, y)\, dy \Big| \leqslant$$

$$\leqslant M |p-p_0| |q-q_0| \Big\{ \int_0^a \int_b^\infty e^{-x \operatorname{Re}(p-p_0) - y \operatorname{Re}(q-q_0)}\, dx\, dy +$$

$$+ \int_a^\infty \int_0^b e^{-x \operatorname{Re}(p-p_0) - y \operatorname{Re}(q-q_0)}\, dx\, dy +$$

$$+ \int_a^\infty \int_b^\infty e^{-x \operatorname{Re}(p-p_0) - y \operatorname{Re}(q-q_0)}\, dx\, dy \Big\} +$$

$$+ M e^{-a \operatorname{Re}(p-p_0) - b \operatorname{Re}(q-q_0)} + M e^{-b \operatorname{Re}(q-q_0)} |p-p_0| \times$$

$$\times \int_0^a e^{-x \operatorname{Re}(p-p_0)}\, dx + M |q-q_0| e^{-a \operatorname{Re}(p-p_0)} \times$$

$$\times \int_0^b e^{-y \operatorname{Re}(q-q_0)}\, dy = M \left[\frac{|p-p_0|}{\operatorname{Re}(p-p_0)} \frac{|q-q_0|}{\operatorname{Re}(q-q_0)} + \frac{|p-p_0|}{\operatorname{Re}(p-p_0)} \right] \times$$

$$\times \left[1 - e^{-a \operatorname{Re}(p-p_0)}\right] e^{-b \operatorname{Re}(q-q_0)} + M \left[\frac{|p-p_0|}{\operatorname{Re}(p-p_0)} \frac{|q-q_0|}{\operatorname{Re}(q-q_0)} + \right.$$

$$\left. + \frac{|q-q_0|}{\operatorname{Re}(q-q_0)} \right] \left[1 - e^{-b \operatorname{Re}(q-q_0)}\right] e^{-a \operatorname{Re}(p-p_0)} +$$

$$+ M \left[\frac{|p-p_0|}{\operatorname{Re}(p-p_0)} \frac{|q-q_0|}{\operatorname{Re}(q-q_0)} + 1 \right] e^{-a \operatorname{Re}(p-p_0) - b \operatorname{Re}(q-q_0)}.$$

Inserting the inequalities

$$\operatorname{Re}(p-p_0) \geqslant |p-p_0| \cos\theta, \quad \operatorname{Re}(p-p_0) \geqslant \delta > 0,$$
$$\operatorname{Re}(q-q_0) \geqslant |q-q_0| \cos\theta, \quad \operatorname{Re}(q-q_0) \geqslant \delta > 0,$$

into this expression we obtain

$$|F(p, q)-F(p, q; a, b)| \leqslant M\left(\frac{1}{\cos^2\theta}+\frac{1}{\cos\theta}\right)e^{-b\delta}+$$

$$+M\left(\frac{1}{\cos^2\theta}+\frac{1}{\cos\theta}\right)e^{-a\delta}+M\left(\frac{1}{\cos^2\theta}+1\right)e^{-a\delta-b\delta}$$

or

$$|F(p, q)-F(p, q; a, b)| \leqslant \frac{2M}{\cos^2\theta}\left(e^{-a\delta}+e^{-b\delta}+e^{-a\delta-b\delta}\right),$$

from which the theorem follows. From this last inequality we derive also:

Corollary. If the integral (1.2) is boundedly convergent at the point (p_0, q_0), then the integrals

$$F(p, q; \infty, b)=\int_0^\infty e^{-px}\,dx\int_0^b e^{-qy} f(x, y)\,dy, \tag{1.8}$$

$$F(p, q; a, \infty)=\int_0^\infty e^{-qy}\,dy\int_0^a e^{-px} f(x, y)\,dx \tag{1.9}$$

converge uniformly as $a\to\infty$ $b\to\infty$ in the region Δ_1, defined in the preceding theorem, and

$$\lim_{b\to\infty} F(p, q; \infty, b)=\lim_{a\to\infty} F(p, q; a, \infty)=F(p, q). \tag{1.10}$$

4. Absolute Convergence

Definition. We shall say that the integral (1.2) is absolutely convergent if

$$\lim_{\substack{a\to\infty\\ b\to\infty}}\int_0^a\int_0^b |e^{-px-qy} f(x, y)|\,dx\,dy=$$

$$=\int_0^\infty\int_0^\infty e^{-\sigma x-\tau y}|f(x, y)|\,dx\,dy,$$

where $\operatorname{Re} p=\sigma$, $\operatorname{Re} q=\tau$.

We have the following theorem.

Theorem 3. If the integral (1.2) converges absolutely at the point (p_0, q_0), then it converges absolutely at all points (p, q) for which

$\mathrm{Re}\,(p - p_0) > 0$ and $\mathrm{Re}\,(q - q_0) > 0.$

The proof of this theorem is analogous to the proof of Theorem 1.

We have defined the region of convergence of the integral (1.2). With the help of Theorem 3 we can in the same way define the region of absolute convergence of this integral.

Theorem 4. If the function $f(x, y)$ satisfies the inequality (1.3), then the integral (1.2) is absolutely convergent at all points (p, q) for which $\mathrm{Re}\,p > h$ and $\mathrm{Re}\,q > k$. Also $|F(p, q)| \leqslant \frac{M}{(\sigma - h)(\tau - k)}$, where $\mathrm{Re}\,p = \sigma$, and $\mathrm{Re}\,q = \tau$.

Proof. In fact

$$\left|\int_0^\infty\int_0^\infty e^{-px-qy} f(x, y)\,dx\,dy\right| \leqslant \int_0^\infty\int_0^\infty |e^{-(\sigma+i\mu)x-(\tau+i\nu)y} \times$$

$$\times f(x, y)|\,dx\,dy \leqslant \int_0^\infty\int_0^\infty M e^{-\sigma x-\tau y} e^{hx+ky}\,dx\,dy = \frac{M}{(\sigma - h)(\tau - k)},$$

as was to be proved.

Remark. Absolute convergence of the integral (1.2) at the point (p_0, q_0) implies bounded convergence at this point, and also at all points (p, q) for which $\mathrm{Re}\,(p - p_0) \geqslant 0$ and $\mathrm{Re}\,(q - q_0) \geqslant 0$, because for such (p, q)

$$|F(p, q; a, b)| \leqslant \int_0^a\int_0^b |e^{-px-qy} f(x, y)|\,dx\,dy \leqslant$$

$$\leqslant \int_0^\infty\int_0^\infty |e^{-p_0x-q_0y} f(x, y)|\,dx\,dy.$$

5. Properties of the Laplace Integral

Theorem 5. The function $F(p, q)$ is analytic in the region D. Moreover

$$\frac{\partial^{m+n}}{\partial p^m\,\partial q^n} F(p, q) = \tag{1.11}$$

$$= (-1)^{m+n} \int_0^\infty\int_0^\infty e^{-px-qy} x^m y^n f(x, y)\,dx\,dy,$$

and the function $x^m y^n f(x, y)$ belongs to the class S.

Proof. If the point (p, q) lies in the region D it follows from Theorem 2 that we can find a bounded closed region Q (containing (p, q) and entirely contained in D) inside which convergence of the integral will be uniformly bounded.

Consequently, the double series

$$F(p, q) = \sum_{k=0}^{\infty} \sum_{l=0}^{\infty} \int_k^{k+1} \int_l^{l+1} e^{-px-qy} f(x, y)\, dx\, dy$$

will converge uniformly in the region Q Each term of this series is an entire function of the variables p, q so that, by a theorem of Weierstrass, the function $F(p, q)$ will be analytic in the region Q; and since (p, q) is an arbitrary point of D, it follows that F will be analytic in the whole of the region D. Also

$$\frac{\partial^{m+n}}{\partial p^m \partial q^n} F(p, q) = (-1)^{m+n} \int_0^{\infty} \int_0^{\infty} e^{-px-qy} x^m y^n f(x, y)\, dx\, dy.$$

If (p_0, q_0) is a point in the region Q, let $\rho > 0$ be the least distance of the point $(\mathrm{Re}\, p_0, \mathrm{Re}\, q_0)$ from the characteristic of convergence (a): then the function $F(p, q)$ is analytic in the region defined by $\mathrm{Re}\, p > \mathrm{Re}\, p_0 - \frac{\rho}{\sqrt{2}}$, $\mathrm{Re}\, q > \mathrm{Re}\, q_0 - \frac{\rho}{\sqrt{2}}$. For sufficiently small values of ρ there exists (according to Theorem 2) a constant $M > 0$ such that $|F(p, q; a, b)| \leqslant M$ for all $a \geqslant 0$, $b \geqslant 0$ and p, q satisfying $|p - p_0| < \frac{\rho}{2}$, $|q - q_0| < \frac{\rho}{2}$. Applying Cauchy's inequality for analytic functions of two variables we obtain

$$\left| \frac{\partial^{m+n}}{\partial p^m \partial q^n} F(p_0, q_0; a, b) \right| \leqslant \frac{M m! n!}{\left(\frac{\rho}{2}\right)^{m+n}},$$

and using the convergence of the integral (1.11), it follows that the function $x^m y^n f(x, y)$ belongs to the class S.

Theorem 6. Let $F_1(p, q)$ and $F_2(p, q)$ be the Laplace transforms of the functions $f_1(x, y)$ and $f_2(x, y)$. If both Laplace integrals converge at the point (p_0, q_0) and

$$F_1(p_0 + nl, q_0 + mk) = F_2(p_0 + nl, q_0 + mk),$$

for $n = 0, 1, 2; \ldots, \ m = 0, 1, 2, \ldots, (l > 0, \ k > 0)$, then $f_1(x, y) = f_2(x, y)$ almost everywhere.

It is clearly sufficient to show that if the Laplace integral

$$F(p, q) = \int_0^\infty \int_0^\infty e^{-px-qy} f(x, y)\, dx\, dy$$

converges at the point (p_0, q_0) and equals zero at the countable sequence of points (p, q) defined by $p = p_0 + nl$ $(n = 0, 1, 2, \ldots)$, $q = q_0 + mk$ $(m = 0, 1, 2, \ldots)$, then $f(x, y) = 0$ almost everywhere.

Proof. We start with equation (1.7):

$$F(p, q) = (p - p_0)(q - q_0) \int_0^\infty \int_0^\infty e^{-(p-p_0)x-(q-q_0)y} \varphi(x, y)\, dx\, dy,$$

where

$$\varphi(x, y) = \int_0^x \int_0^y e^{-p_0\xi - q_0\eta} f(\xi, \eta)\, d\xi\, d\eta.$$

The hypothesis of the theorem becomes

$$\int_0^\infty \int_0^\infty e^{-nlx-mky} \varphi(x, y)\, dx\, dy = 0$$

$$(n = 1, 2, \ldots;\quad m = 1, 2, \ldots).$$

After the change of variable

$$u = e^{-xl}, \quad v = e^{-yk},$$

we obtain

$$\int_0^1 \int_0^1 u^{n-1} v^{m-1} \psi(u, v)\, du\, dv = 0, \tag{1.12}$$

where

$$\psi(u, v) = \varphi\left(-\frac{\ln u}{l}, -\frac{\ln v}{k}\right).$$

The function $\psi(u, v)$ is clearly continuous on the square $(0 < u < 1, 0 < v < 1)$. The system of functions $u^n v^m$ $(n = 0, 1, 2, \ldots;$ $m = 0, 1, 2, \ldots)$ is complete so that it follows from (1.12) that

$\psi(u, v) \equiv 0$ for $0 < u < 1, \quad 0 < v < 1$ and hence that $\varphi(x, y) = 0$ for $< x < \infty, \; 0 < y < \infty$: i.e.

$$\int_0^x \int_0^y e^{-p_0\xi - q_0\eta} f(\xi, \eta)\, d\xi\, d\eta = 0$$

$$(0 \leqslant x \leqslant \infty, \; 0 \leqslant y \leqslant \infty).$$

Consequently, $f(x, y) = 0$ almost everywhere.

Remark. A Laplace transform $F(p, q)$ which is not identically zero can have only a finite number of zeros in points (p, q) specified by arithmetic progressions, and it is uniquely defined by its values at an infinite sequence of points $p = p_0 + nl$, $q = q_0 + mk$, (where l, k are positive real numbers and m, n run through the non-negative integers).

Theorem 7. If the integral (1.2) converges absolutely for $\operatorname{Re} p > \sigma_0$ and $\operatorname{Re} q > \tau_0$, then

$$\lim_{\substack{\mu \to \pm\infty \\ \nu \to \pm\infty}} F(\sigma + i\mu, \tau + i\nu) = 0$$

and the convergence is uniform for all

$$\sigma\,(\sigma \geqslant \sigma_1 > \sigma_0), \quad \tau\,(\tau \geqslant \tau_1 > \tau_0).$$

Proof. From the absolute convergence of the integral (1.2) and from the inequality

$$|F(p, q)| \leqslant \left| \int_0^A \int_0^B e^{-px-qy} f(x, y)\, dx\, dy \right| +$$

$$+ \int_0^A \int_B^\infty e^{-\sigma_1 x - \tau_1 y} |f(x, y)|\, dx\, dy +$$

$$+ \int_A^\infty \int_0^B e^{-\sigma_1 x - \tau_1 y} |f(x, y)|\, dx\, dy + \int_A^\infty \int_B^\infty e^{-\sigma_1 x - \tau_1 y} |f(x, y)|\, dx\, dy$$

it follows that it is sufficient to prove the theorem for the function

$$F(p, q) = \int_0^A \int_0^B e^{-px-qy} f(x, y)\, dx\, dy\,.$$

where A and B are arbitrary positive numbers. If the first order and the mixed second order partial derivatives of $f(x, y)$ are absolutely integrable, then it is easy to establish the validity of Theorem 7 by integration by parts. The general form of Theorem 7 follows from the fact that, given $\varepsilon > 0$, we can find a function $f_1(x, y)$ which has continuous first and second order partial derivatives and which satisfies

$$\int_0^A \int_0^B |f(x, y) - f_1(x, y)| e^{-\sigma_1 x - \tau_1 y} \, dx \, dy < \varepsilon,$$

Theorem 8. If the integral (1.2) converges boundedly at the point (p, q) and $\operatorname{Re} p = \alpha > 0$, $\operatorname{Re} q = \beta > 0$ then for $a \geqslant 0$, $b \geqslant 0$

$$\left| e^{-\alpha a - \beta b} \int_0^a \int_0^b f(\xi, \eta) \, d\xi \, d\eta \right| < M,$$

and

$$\lim_{\substack{a \to \infty \\ b \to \infty}} e^{-\alpha a - \beta b} \int_0^a \int_0^b f(x, y) \, dx \, dy = 0.$$

Proof. Integrating by parts we derive

$$\int_0^a \int_0^b f(\xi, \eta) \, d\xi \, d\eta =$$

$$= \int_0^a d\xi \int_0^b e^{qy} \frac{\partial}{\partial y} \left[\int_0^y f(\xi, \eta) e^{-q\eta} \, d\eta - \int_0^b f(\xi, \eta) e^{-q\eta} \, d\eta \right] dy =$$

$$= \int_0^a d\xi \left\{ \left[\int_0^y f(\xi, \eta) e^{-q\eta} \, d\eta - \int_0^b f(\xi, \eta) e^{-q\eta} \, d\eta \right] e^{qy} \Bigg|_0^b - \right.$$

$$\left. - q \int_0^b e^{qy} \left[\int_0^y f(\xi, \eta) e^{-q\eta} \, d\eta - \int_0^b f(\xi, \eta) e^{-q\eta} \right] dy \right\} =$$

$$= \int_0^a d\xi \left\{ \int_0^b f(\xi, \eta) e^{-q\eta} \, d\eta - \right.$$

$$\left. - q \int_0^b e^{qy} \left[\int_0^y f(\xi, \eta) e^{-q\eta} \, d\eta - \int_0^b f(\xi, \eta) e^{-q\eta} \, d\eta \right] dy \right\}.$$

Recalling the function

$$\varphi(x, y) = \int_0^x \int_0^y e^{-p\xi - q\eta} f(\xi, \eta)\, d\xi\, d\eta.$$

the preceding equality can be written in the form

$$\int_0^a \int_0^b f(\xi, \eta)\, d\xi\, d\eta = \int_0^a e^{px} \frac{\partial}{\partial x} [\varphi(x, b) - \varphi(a, b)]\, dx$$

$$-q \int_0^b e^{qy}\, dy \left\{ \int_0^a e^{px} \frac{\partial}{\partial x} [\varphi(x, y) - \varphi(x, b) - \varphi(a, y) + \right.$$

$$\left. + \varphi(a, b)]\, dx \right\}.$$

Integrating once more by parts, we obtain

$$\int_0^a \int_0^b f(\xi, \eta)\, d\xi\, d\eta = [\varphi(x, b) - \varphi(a, b)]\, e^{px} \Big|_0^a -$$

$$- p \int_0^a e^{px} [\varphi(x, b) - \varphi(a, b)]\, dx - q \int_0^b e^{qy} \times$$

$$\times \left\{ [\varphi(x, y) - \varphi(x, b) - \varphi(a, y) + \varphi(a, b)]\, e^{px} \Big|_0^a - \right.$$

$$\left. - p \int_0^a e^{px} [\varphi(x, y) - \varphi(x, b) - \varphi(a, y) + \varphi(a, b)]\, dx \right\} dy =$$

$$= \varphi(a, b) - p \int_0^a [\varphi(x, b) - \varphi(a, b)]\, e^{px}\, dx -$$

$$- q \int_0^b [\varphi(a, y) - \varphi(a, b)]\, e^{qy}\, dy +$$

$$+ pq \int_0^a \int_0^b [\varphi(x, y) - \varphi(x, b) - \varphi(a, y) + \varphi(a, b)]\, e^{px + qy}\, dx\, dy.$$

Because the integral (1.2) is assumed convergent at the point (p, q) we have $|\varphi(x, y)| < M$ and

$$\lim_{\substack{x \to \infty \\ y \to \infty}} \varphi(x, y) = \int_0^\infty \int_0^\infty e^{-p\xi - q\eta} f(\xi, \eta)\, d\xi\, d\eta$$

exists. Hence, if $\varepsilon > 0$ is given, we can choose constants A and B so that $|\varphi(x, y) - \varphi(a, b)| < \varepsilon$ for $x > A,\ y > B,\ a > A,\ b > B$. For any pair of numbers $a > A,\ b > B$ we have

$$e^{-\alpha a-\beta b}\int_0^a\int_0^b f(\xi,\eta)\,d\xi\,d\eta = \Big\{\varphi(a,b) - p\int_0^A [\varphi(x,b)-\varphi(a,b)]\times$$

$$\times e^{px}\,dx - q\int_0^B [\varphi(a,y)-\varphi(a,b)]\,e^{qy}\,dy +$$

$$+ pq\int_0^A\int_0^B [\varphi(x,y)-\varphi(x,b)-\varphi(a,y)+\varphi(a,b)]\times$$

$$\times e^{px+qy}\,dx\,dy\Big\}e^{-\alpha a-\beta b} + \Big\{-p\int_A^a [\varphi(x,b)-\varphi(a,b)]\,e^{px}\,dx -$$

$$- q\int_B^b [\varphi(a,y)-\varphi(a,b)]\,e^{qy}\,dy + pq\Big(\int_0^A\int_B^b + \int_A^a\int_0^B +$$

$$+ \int_A^a\int_B^b\Big)[\varphi(x,y)-\varphi(x,b)-\varphi(a,y)+\varphi(a,b)]\times$$

$$\times e^{px+qy}\,dx\,dy\Big\}e^{-\alpha a-\beta b}.$$

From the existence of $\lim\limits_{\substack{x\to\infty\\ y\to\infty}} \varphi(x, y)$ we can also aver that $|\varphi(a, y)-\varphi(a, b)| < \varepsilon$, $|\varphi(x, b)-\varphi(a, b)| < \varepsilon$, and $|\varphi(x, y)-\varphi(x, b)-\varphi(a, y)+\varphi(a, b)| < 2\varepsilon$, for $x > A$, $y > B$, $a > A$, $b > B$. Consequently

$$\left|e^{-\alpha a-\beta b}\int_0^a\int_0^b f(\xi,\eta)\,d\xi\,d\eta\right| \leqslant Q\Big(e^{-\alpha a-\beta b} + e^{-\alpha a-\beta b}\int_A^a e^{\alpha x}\,dx +$$

$$+ e^{-\alpha a-\beta b}\int_B^b e^{\beta y}\,dy\Big) + |pq|\,2\varepsilon e^{-\alpha a-\beta b}\int_A^a\int_B^b e^{\alpha x+\beta y}\,dx\,dy. \qquad (1.13)$$

Here Q is a constant independent of a and b satisfying the condition

$$\Big|\varphi(a,b) - p\int_0^A [\varphi(x,b)-\varphi(a,b)]\,e^{px}\,dx -$$

$$-q\int_0^B [\varphi(a, y)-\varphi(a, b)]\, e^{qy}\, dy+$$

$$\left.+pq\int_0^A\int_0^B [\varphi(x, y)-\varphi(x, b)-\varphi(a, y)+\varphi(a, b)]\, e^{px+qy}\, dx\, dy\right| \leqslant$$

$$\leqslant M+2M|p|\int_0^A e^{\alpha x}\, dx+2M|q|\int_0^B e^{\beta y}\, dy+$$

$$+4M|pq|\int_0^A\int_0^B e^{\alpha x+\beta y}\, dx\, dy \leqslant Q.$$

It follows from (1.13) that the expression

$$e^{-\alpha a-\beta b}\int_0^a\int_0^b f(\xi, \eta)\, d\xi\, d\eta$$

is bounded for all $a \geqslant 0$, $b \geqslant 0$, and that

$$\lim_{\substack{a\to\infty \\ b\to\infty}}\left|e^{-\alpha a-\beta b}\int_0^a\int_0^b f(\xi, \eta)\, d\xi\, d\eta\right| < 2\varepsilon|p||q|.$$

Theorem 9. In order that $f(x, y)$ shall belong to the class S, it is necessary and sufficient that the inequality

$$\left|e^{-\alpha a-\beta b}\int_0^a\int_0^b f(x, y)\, dx\, dy\right| < M \quad (a \geqslant 0,\ b \geqslant 0) \quad (1.14)$$

holds for one pair of values (α, β) - $\alpha > 0$, $\beta > 0$.

Proof: If the function $f(x, y)$ belongs to the class S, then by Theorem 1, there is a point (p, q) such that the integral converges boundedly at the point ($\text{Re}\, p=\alpha > 0, \text{Re}\, q=\beta > 0$) and condition (1.14) follows from the preceding theorem.

Conversely, if (1.14) holds and the point (p, q) is chosen so that $\text{Re}\, p > \alpha$, $\text{Re}\, q > \beta$ we obtain from (1.4), with $p_0=q_0=0$,

$$F(p, q; a, b)=e^{-pa-qb}\varphi(a, b)+pe^{-qb}\int_0^a \varphi(x, b)\, e^{-px}\, dx+$$

$$+qe^{-pa}\int_0^b e^{-qy}\varphi(a, y)\,dy + pq\int_0^a\int_0^b e^{-px-qy}\varphi(x, y)\,dx\,dy, \tag{1.15}$$

where

$$\varphi(x, y) = \int_0^x\int_0^y f(\xi, \eta)\,d\xi\,d\eta.$$

The condition (1.14) may be written in terms of the function $\varphi(x, y)$ as $|\varphi(x, y)e^{-\alpha x-\beta y}| < M$ for all $x \geqslant 0$, $y \geqslant 0$. From this it follows that the integral (1.2) is boundedly convergent at the point (p, q), if $\operatorname{Re} p > \alpha$, $\operatorname{Re} q > \beta$. We also have

$$\int_0^\infty\int_0^\infty e^{-px-qy}f(x, y)\,dx\,dy = pq\int_0^\infty\int_0^\infty e^{-px-qy}\varphi(x, y)\,dx\,dy \tag{1.16}$$

when $\operatorname{Re} p > \alpha$, $\operatorname{Re} q > \beta$.

It is known for the ordinary Laplace transform that to each operation on a determining function there corresponds an operation on the generating function, and conversely that an operation performed on a generating function is reflected in an operation on the determining function. The double Laplace transform exhibits the same behaviour. For example, it follows from Theorem 5 that differentiation of a generating function corresponds to multiplication of the determining function by $(-x)$ or $(-y)$. We should emphasize that the set of all possible operations on functions of two variables is incomparably greater than that on functions of one variable, since there are many operations on functions of two variables which have no one-dimensional analogues: e.g. the operations which transform the function $F(p, q)$ into $F(p, p)$ or into $\dfrac{F(p, q)-F(q, p)}{p-q}$. Thus the possibilities for the application of the double Laplace transform are much wider.

Theorem 10. If the function $f(x, y)$ belongs to the class S, then the function

$$f_{u,v}(x, y) = \begin{cases} f(x-u, y-v) & \text{for } x > u,\ y > v \\ 0 - & \text{otherwise} \end{cases} \qquad (u, v > 0)$$

also belongs to the class S, and

$$\int_0^\infty e^{-px}dx\int_0^\infty e^{-qy}f_{u,v}(x, y)\,dy =$$

$$= e^{-pu-qv}\int_0^\infty e^{-px}\,dx\int_0^\infty e^{-qy}f(x,\ y)\,dy.$$

Proof: In fact, we have

$$\int_0^a\int_0^b e^{-px-qy}f_{u,v}(x,\ y)\,dx\,dy =$$

$$= \int_u^a\int_v^b e^{-px-qy}f(x-u,\ y-v)\,dx\,dy =$$

$$= \int_0^{a-u} e^{-p(u+x)}\,dx\int_0^{b-v} e^{-q(v+y)}f(x,\ y)\,dy, \qquad (1.17)$$

from which it follows that the integral (1.17) is bounded for all $a \geqslant 0,\ b \geqslant 0$ and therefore that the limit exists and is equal to

$$\lim_{\substack{a\to\infty\\ b\to\infty}}\int_0^a\int_0^b e^{-px-qy}f_{u,v}(x,\ y)\,dx\,dy =$$

$$= \int_0^\infty e^{-px}\,dx\int_0^\infty e^{-qy}f_{u,v}(x,\ y)\,dy =$$

$$= e^{-pu-qv}\int_0^\infty e^{-px}\,dx\int_0^\infty e^{-qy}f(x,\ y)\,dy,$$

which was to be proved.

Remark. If $f(x,\ y)$ belongs to S and $f(x,\ y)\equiv 0$ for $0 < x < s, 0 < y < t$ then the function $f(x+u,\ y+v)$ also belongs to S if $0 < u \leqslant s,\ 0 < v \leqslant t$ and we have

$$\int_0^\infty\int_0^\infty e^{-px-qy}f(x+u,\ y+v)\,dx\,dy =$$

$$= e^{pu+qv}\int_0^\infty\int_0^\infty e^{-px-qy}f(x,\ y)\,dx\,dy.$$

Theorem 11. Let $F(p,\ q)$ be the Laplace transform of the function $f(x,\ y)$ and suppose that the integral

$$H(p) = \int_0^\infty e^{-pt} h(t)\, dt$$

is absolutely convergent. Then

$$H(p+q) F(p, q) = \int_0^\infty \int_0^\infty e^{-px-qy} g(x, y)\, dx\, dy,$$

where

$$g(x, y) = \int_0^{\min(x, y)} h(\tau) f(x-\tau, y-\tau)\, d\tau.$$

Proof. We introduce the change of variables $x-\tau=\xi$, $\tau=\tau$, $y-\tau=\eta$, which yields

$$\int_0^\infty \int_0^\infty e^{-px-qy}\, dx\, dy \int_0^{\min(x, y)} h(\tau) f(x-\tau, y-\tau)\, d\tau =$$

$$= \int_0^\infty \int_0^\infty \int_0^\infty e^{-p\xi-q\eta-(p+q)\tau} h(\tau) f(\xi, \eta)\, d\xi\, d\eta\, d\tau =$$

$$= \int_0^\infty e^{-(p+q)\tau} h(\tau)\, d\tau \int_0^\infty \int_0^\infty e^{-p\xi-q\eta} f(\xi, \eta)\, d\xi\, d\eta = H(p+q) F(p, q)$$

and the theorem is proved.

If the derivatives of the function $f(x, y)$ belong to the class S, then their Laplace transforms can be found by integrating by parts. For example, if $f'_x(x, y)$ belongs to S we integrate by parts and use (1.8) (1.9), (1.10) to obtain

$$\int_0^\infty e^{-qy}\, dy \int_0^\infty e^{-px} f'_x(x, y)\, dx = \int_0^\infty e^{-qy} \left\{ e^{-px} f(x, y) \Big|_{x=0}^{x=\infty} + \right.$$

$$\left. + p \int_0^\infty e^{-px} f(x, y)\, dx \right\} dy = pF(p, q) - \int_0^\infty e^{-qy} f(0, y)\, dy$$

We may extend this: if all partial derivatives of the function $f(x, y)$ belong to S, up to the n-th order in x, the m-th order in y, and mixed derivatives up to the $(m+n)$-th order, then in the same way

$$\int_0^\infty e^{-px}\,dx\int_0^\infty e^{-qy}f'_y(x, y)\,dy = qF(p, q) - \int_0^\infty e^{-px}f(x, 0)\,dx,$$

$$\int_0^\infty e^{-px}\,dx\int_0^\infty e^{-qy}f''_{xy}(x, y)\,dy = pqF(p, q) -$$

$$-\int_0^\infty e^{-px}f'_x(x, 0)\,dx - \int_0^\infty e^{-qy}f'_y(0, y)\,dy - f(0, 0),$$

$$\int_0^\infty e^{-px}\,dx\int_0^\infty e^{-qy}f''_{yy}(x, y)\,dy =$$

$$= q^2F(p, q) - \int_0^\infty e^{-px}\left\{qf(x, 0) + f'_y(x, 0)\right\}dx,$$

$$\int_0^\infty e^{-qy}\,dy\int_0^\infty e^{-px}f''_{xx}(x, y)\,dx =$$

$$= p^2F(p, q) - \int_0^\infty e^{-qy}\left\{pf(0, y) + f'_x(0, y)\right\}dy.$$

. . . .

$$\int_0^\infty e^{-qy}\,dy\int_0^\infty e^{-px}f^{(n)}_{x^n}(x, y)\,dx = p^nF(p, q) -$$

$$-\int_0^\infty e^{-qy}\left\{p^{n-1}f(0, y) + p^{n-2}f'_x(0,y) + \ldots\right.$$

$$\left.\ldots + f^{(n-1)}_{x^{n-1}}(0, y)\right\}dy = p^nF(p, q) -$$

$$-\int_0^\infty e^{-qy}\sum_{k=0}^{n-1} p^{n-k-1}f^{(k)}_{x^k}(0, y)\,dy,$$

$$\int_0^\infty e^{-px}\,dx\int_0^\infty e^{-qy}f^{(m)}_{y^m}(x, y)\,dy = q^mF(p, q) -$$

$$-\int_0^\infty e^{-px}\left\{q^{m-1}f(x, 0) + q^{m-2}f'_y(x, 0) + \ldots\right.$$

$$\left.\ldots + f^{(m-1)}_{y^{(m-1)}}(x, 0)\right\}dx = q^mF(p, q) -$$

$$-\int_0^\infty e^{-px}\sum_{k=0}^{m-1} q^{m-k-1} f_{y^k}^{(k)}(x, 0)\,dx,$$

$$\int_0^\infty e^{-px}\,dx \int_0^\infty e^{-qy} f_{x^n y^m}^{(n+m)}(x, y)\,dy = p^n q^m F(p, q) -$$

$$-\sum_{r=0}^{n-1}\sum_{k=0}^{m-1} p^{n-r-1} q^{m-k-1} f_{x^r y^k}^{(r+k)}(0,0) +$$

$$+\int_0^\infty e^{-px}\sum_{k=0}^{m-1} q^{m-k-1} f_{x^n y^k}^{(k+n)}(x, 0)\,dx +$$

$$+\int_0^\infty e^{-qy}\sum_{r=0}^{n-1} p^{n-r-1} f_{x^r y^m}^{(r+m)}(0, y)\,dy.$$

6. Convolutions

The theorem on convolutions, which is well-known for one-dimensional Laplace transforms, may be extended to the two-dimensional case in two ways.

Theorem 12. If, at the point (p, q) the integral

$$F_1(p, q) = \int_0^\infty\int_0^\infty e^{-px-qy} f_1(x, y)\,dx\,dy$$

is boundedly convergent, and the integral

$$F_2(p, q) = \int_0^\infty\int_0^\infty e^{-px-qy} f_2(x, y)\,dx\,dy \qquad (1.18)$$

is absolutely convergent, then $F(p, q) = F_1(p, q)\,F_2(p, q)$ is the Laplace transform of the function

$$f(x, y) = \int_0^x\int_0^y f_1(x-\xi, y-\eta)\,f_2(\xi, \eta)\,d\xi\,d\eta$$

and the integral

$$F(p, q) = \int_0^\infty\int_0^\infty e^{-px-qy} f(x, y)\,dx\,dy$$

is boundedly convergent at the point (p, q) i.e. the function $f(x, y)$ belongs to the class S.

Proof. Making the change of variables $x-\xi=u$, $y-\eta=v$, we have (for all $a \geqslant 0$, $b \geqslant 0$)

$$\int_0^b e^{-qy}\,dy \int_0^a e^{-px} f(x, y)\,dx =$$

$$= \int_0^b e^{-qy}\,dy \int_0^a e^{-px}\,dx \int_0^x d\xi \int_0^y f_2(\xi, \eta) f_1(x-\xi, y-\eta)\,d\eta =$$

$$= \int_0^b d\eta \int_0^a f_2(\xi, \eta)\,d\xi \int_\eta^b e^{-qy}\,dy \int_\xi^a e^{-px} f_1(x-\xi, y-\eta)\,dx =$$

$$= \int_0^b e^{-q\eta}\,d\eta \int_0^a e^{-p\xi} f_2(\xi, \eta)\,d\xi \int_0^{b-\eta} e^{-qv}\,dv \int_0^{a-\xi} e^{-pu} f_1(u, v)\,du =$$

$$= \int_0^b e^{-q\eta}\,d\eta \int_0^a e^{-p\xi} f_2(\xi, \eta)\,d\xi \int_0^b e^{-qv}\,dv \int_0^a e^{-pu} f_1(u, v)\,du -$$

$$- \int_0^b e^{-q\eta}\,d\eta \int_0^a e^{-p\xi} f_2(\xi, \eta)\,\rho_1(\xi, \eta; a, b)\,d\xi,$$

where

$$\rho_1(\xi, \eta; a, b) = \int_0^b e^{-qv}\,dv \int_0^a e^{-pu} f_1(u, v)\,du -$$

$$- \int_0^{b-\eta} e^{-qv}\,dv \int_0^{a-\xi} e^{-pu} f_1(u, v)\,du. \tag{1.19}$$

We shall write

$J_1(p, q; a, b) =$

$$= \int_0^b e^{-q\eta}\,d\eta \int_0^a e^{-p\xi} f_2(\xi, \eta)\,d\xi \int_0^b e^{-qv}\,dv \int_0^a e^{-pu} f_1(u, v)\,du,$$

$$J_2(p, q; a, b) = \int_0^b e^{-q\eta}\,d\eta \int_0^a e^{-p\xi} f_2(\xi, \eta)\,\rho_1(\xi, \eta; a, b)\,d\xi.$$

Because the functions $f_1(x, y)$ and $f_2(x, y)$ belong to the class S, we have

$$|J_1(p, q; a, b)| < M_1,$$

for all $a \geqslant 0,\ b \geqslant 0$ and the limit

$$\lim_{\substack{a \to \infty \\ b \to \infty}} J_1(p, q; a, b) = F_1(p, q) F_2(p, q).$$

exists. Since $|\rho_1(\xi, \eta; a, b)| < M$, it follows from the absolute convergence of the integral (1.18) that for all $a \geqslant 0,\ b \geqslant 0$

$$|J_2(p, q; a, b)| < M_2.$$

Consequently, our theorem is proved if we can show that

$$\lim_{\substack{a \to \infty \\ b \to \infty}} J_2(p, q; a, b) = 0.$$

We have

$$\begin{aligned} J_2(p, q; a, b) &= \int_0^b e^{-q\eta}\, d\eta \int_0^a e^{-p\xi} f_2(\xi, \eta)\, \rho_1(\xi, \eta; a, b)\, d\xi = \\ &= \int_0^{\frac{b}{2}} e^{-q\eta}\, d\eta \int_0^{\frac{a}{2}} e^{-p\xi} f_2(\xi, \eta)\, \rho_1(\xi, \eta; a, b)\, d\xi + \\ &+ \int_0^b e^{-q\eta}\, d\eta \int_0^a e^{-p\xi} f_2(\xi, \eta)\, \rho_1(\xi, \eta; a, b)\, d\xi - \\ &- \int_0^{\frac{b}{2}} e^{-q\eta}\, d\eta \int_0^{\frac{a}{2}} e^{-p\xi} f_2(\xi, \eta)\, \rho_1(\xi, \eta; a, b)\, d\xi. \end{aligned} \tag{1.20}$$

If we write

$$\mu(a, b) = \max_{\substack{0 \leqslant \xi \leqslant \frac{a}{2} \\ 0 \leqslant \eta \leqslant \frac{b}{2}}} |\rho_1(\xi, \eta; a, b)|,$$

we deduce from the fact that the function $f_1(x, y)$ belongs to S, that

$$\lim_{\substack{a \to \infty \\ b \to \infty}} \mu(a, b) = 0. \tag{1.21}$$

From equations (1.18), (1.20) and (1.21) we obtain

$$\lim_{\substack{a \to \infty \\ b \to \infty}} \int_0^{\frac{b}{2}} e^{-q\eta}\, d\eta \int_0^{\frac{a}{2}} e^{-p\xi} f_2(\xi, \eta)\, \rho_1(\xi, \eta; a, b)\, d\xi = 0, \tag{1.22}$$

and it follows from the absolute convergence of the integral (1.18) and the boundedness of $\rho_1(\xi, \eta; a, b)$ that

$$\lim_{\substack{a \to \infty \\ b \to \infty}} \left\{ \int_0^b e^{-q\eta}\, d\eta \int_0^a e^{-p\xi} f_2(\xi, \eta)\, \rho_1(\xi, \eta; a, b)\, d\xi - \right.$$

$$\left. - \int_0^{\frac{b}{2}} e^{-q\eta}\, d\eta \int_0^{\frac{a}{2}} e^{-p\xi} f_2(\xi, \eta)\, \rho_1(\xi, \eta; a, b)\, d\xi \right\} = 0,$$

therefore

$$\lim_{\substack{a \to \infty \\ b \to \infty}} J_2(p, q; a, b) = 0.$$

Theorem 13. If the integral

$$F(p, q) = \int_0^\infty \int_0^\infty e^{-px-qy} f(x, y)\, dx\, dy$$

converges boundedly at the point (p, q) and if the integral

$$G(p\cos\alpha + q\sin\alpha) = \int_0^\infty e^{-(p\cos\alpha + q\sin\alpha)t}\, g(t)\, dt, \tag{1.23}$$

$$\left(0 \leqslant \alpha \leqslant \frac{\pi}{2}\right)$$

is absolutely convergent, then $\Phi(p, q) = G(p\cos\alpha + q\sin\alpha) F(p, q)$ is the Laplace transform of

$$\varphi(x, y) =$$

$$= \begin{cases} \left.\begin{aligned} &\frac{1}{\cos\alpha}\int\limits_0^{x} g\left(\frac{\xi}{\cos\alpha}\right) f(x-\xi,\, y-\xi\operatorname{tg}\alpha)\, d\xi = \\ &= \frac{1}{\sin\alpha}\int\limits_0^{x\operatorname{tg}\alpha} g\left(\frac{\eta}{\sin\alpha}\right) f\left(x-\frac{\eta}{\operatorname{tg}\alpha},\, y-\eta\right) d\eta \end{aligned}\right\} & (y \geqslant x\operatorname{tg}\alpha), \\ \left.\begin{aligned} &\frac{1}{\cos\alpha}\int\limits_0^{\frac{y}{\operatorname{tg}\alpha}} g\left(\frac{\xi}{\cos\alpha}\right) f(x-\xi,\, y-\xi\operatorname{tg}\alpha)\, d\xi = \\ &= \frac{1}{\sin\alpha}\int\limits_0^{y} g\left(\frac{\eta}{\sin\alpha}\right) f\left(x-\frac{\eta}{\operatorname{tg}\alpha},\, y-\eta\right) d\eta \end{aligned}\right\} & (y \leqslant x\operatorname{tg}\alpha), \end{cases}$$

and the integral

$$\Phi(p, q) = \int\limits_0^{\infty}\int\limits_0^{\infty} e^{-px-qy}\varphi(x, y)\, dx\, dy$$

is boundedly convergent at the point (p, q), i.e. the function $\varphi(x, y)$ belongs to the class S.

Proof. We have to consider two cases:

(1) $\alpha \neq \frac{\pi}{2}$;

(2) $\alpha = \frac{\pi}{2}$.

Case (1) $\alpha \neq \frac{\pi}{2}$). Let

$$\varphi(x, y) = \begin{cases} \dfrac{1}{\cos\alpha}\displaystyle\int\limits_0^{x} g\left(\frac{\xi}{\cos\alpha}\right) f(x-\xi,\, y-\xi\operatorname{tg}\alpha)\, d\xi & \text{for } y \geqslant x\operatorname{tg}\alpha, \\ \dfrac{1}{\cos\alpha}\displaystyle\int\limits_0^{\frac{y}{\operatorname{tg}\alpha}} g\left(\frac{\xi}{\cos\alpha}\right) f(x-\xi,\, y-\xi\operatorname{tg}\alpha)\, d\xi & \text{for } y \leqslant x\operatorname{tg}\alpha. \end{cases}$$

Then, for $b \geqslant a\operatorname{tg}\alpha$, we will have

$$\int\limits_0^{b} e^{-qy}\, dy \int\limits_0^{a} e^{-px}\varphi(x, y)\, dx =$$

$$=\frac{1}{\cos\alpha}\int_0^b e^{-qy}dy\int_0^a g\left(\frac{\xi}{\cos\alpha}\right)d\xi\int_\xi^a e^{-px}f(x-\xi,\ y-\xi\operatorname{tg}\alpha)\,dx=$$

$$=\frac{1}{\cos\alpha}\int_0^a g\left(\frac{\xi}{\cos\alpha}\right)d\xi\int_0^b e^{-qy}dy\int_\xi^a e^{-px}f(x-\xi,\ y-\xi\operatorname{tg}\alpha)\,dx=$$

$$=\frac{1}{\cos\alpha}\int_0^a e^{-p\xi}g\left(\frac{\xi}{\cos\alpha}\right)d\xi\int_0^{a-\xi} e^{-pu}du\int_0^b e^{-qy}f(u,y-\xi\operatorname{tg}\alpha)\,dy=$$

$$=\frac{1}{\cos\alpha}\int_0^a e^{-(p+q\operatorname{tg}\alpha)\xi}g\left(\frac{\xi}{\cos\alpha}\right)d\xi\int_0^{a-\xi} e^{-pu}du\int_0^{b-\xi\operatorname{tg}\alpha} e^{-qv}f(u,v)\,dv=$$

$$=\frac{1}{\cos\alpha}\int_0^a e^{-(p+q\operatorname{tg}\alpha)\xi}g\left(\frac{\xi}{\cos\alpha}\right)d\xi\int_0^a e^{-pu}du\int_0^b e^{-qv}f(u,v)\,dv-$$

$$-\frac{1}{\cos\alpha}\int_0^a e^{-(p+q\operatorname{tg}\alpha)\xi}g\left(\frac{\xi}{\cos\alpha}\right)\rho_2(\xi;\ a,\ b)\,d\xi, \tag{1.24}$$

where

$$\rho_2(\xi;\ a,\ b)=\int_0^b e^{-qv}dv\int_0^a e^{-pu}f(u,\ v)\,du-$$

$$-\int_0^{a-\xi} e^{-pu}du\int_0^{b-\xi\operatorname{tg}\alpha} e^{-qv}f(u,\ v)\,dv.$$

Using arguments analogous to those which we used in Theorem 12 we can show that

$$\lim_{\substack{a\to\infty\\ b\to\infty}}\frac{1}{\cos\alpha}\int_0^a e^{-(p+q\operatorname{tg}\alpha)\xi}g\left(\frac{\xi}{\cos\alpha}\right)\rho_2(\xi;\ a,\ b)\,d\xi=0 \tag{1.25}$$

and

$$\lim_{\substack{a\to\infty\\ b\to\infty}}\frac{1}{\cos\alpha}\int_0^a e^{-(p+q\operatorname{tg}\alpha)\xi}g\left(\frac{\xi}{\cos\alpha}\right)d\xi\int_0^a e^{-pu}du\int_0^b e^{-qv}f(u,\ v)dv=$$

$$= \lim_{\substack{a\to\infty \\ b\to\infty}} \int_0^{\frac{a}{\cos\alpha}} e^{-(p\cos\alpha+q\sin\alpha)\,t} g(t)\,dt \int_0^a e^{-pu}\,du \int_0^b e^{-qv} f(u, v)\,dv =$$

$$= G(p\cos\alpha + q\sin\alpha)\,F(p, q). \tag{1.26}$$

From (1.24), (1.25), and (1.26) it follows that when $b \geqslant a \operatorname{tg}\alpha$

$$\lim_{\substack{a\to\infty \\ b\to\infty}} \int_0^b e^{-qy}\,dy \int_0^a e^{-px} \varphi(x, y)\,dx = \\ = G(p\cos\alpha + q\sin\alpha)\,F(p, q). \tag{1.27}$$

When $b \leqslant a \operatorname{tg}\alpha$ we can show in the same way that

$$\lim_{\substack{a\to\infty \\ b\to\infty}} \int_0^b e^{-qy}\,dy \int_0^a e^{-px} \varphi(x, y)\,dx =$$

$$= \lim_{\substack{a\to\infty \\ b\to\infty}} \frac{1}{\cos\alpha} \int_0^{\frac{b}{\operatorname{tg}\alpha}} e^{-(p+q\operatorname{tg}\alpha)\xi} g\left(\frac{\xi}{\cos\alpha}\right) d\xi \times$$

$$\times \int_0^{a-\xi} e^{-pu}\,du \int_0^{b-\xi\operatorname{tg}\alpha} e^{-qv} f(u, v)\,dv = G(p\cos\alpha + q\sin\alpha)\,F(p, q),$$

and the proof is complete.

Case (2) $\alpha = \frac{\pi}{2}$. When $\alpha = \frac{\pi}{2}$, we write $\varphi(x, y)$ in the form

$$\varphi(x, y) = \begin{cases} \dfrac{1}{\sin\alpha} \displaystyle\int_0^{x\operatorname{tg}\alpha} g\left(\frac{\eta}{\sin\alpha}\right) f\left(x - \frac{\eta}{\operatorname{tg}\alpha},\ y - \eta\right) d\eta & \text{for } y \geqslant x\operatorname{tg}\alpha, \\ \dfrac{1}{\sin\alpha} \displaystyle\int_0^{y} g\left(\frac{\eta}{\sin\alpha}\right) f\left(x - \frac{\eta}{\operatorname{tg}\alpha},\ y - \eta\right) d\eta & \text{for } y \leqslant x\operatorname{tg}\alpha, \end{cases}$$

and the proof goes through in the same way as before.

7. The Inversion Theorem

Theorem 14. We shall suppose that the function $f(x, y)$ has first order partial derivatives $f'_x(x, y)$ $f'_y(x, y)$ and mixed second order partial derivative $f''_{xy}(x, y)$ and that we can find positive constants Q, k_1, k_2, such that for all $0 < x < \infty$, $0 < y < \infty$

$$|f(x, y)| < Qe^{k_1 x + k_2 y}, \quad |f''_{xy}(x, y)| < Qe^{k_1 x + k_2 y}. \tag{1.28}$$

Then, if

$$F(p, q) = \int_0^\infty \int_0^\infty e^{-px-qy} f(x, y)\, dx\, dy, \tag{1.29}$$

we have

$$f(x, y) = \lim_{\substack{\omega_1 \to \infty \\ \omega_2 \to \infty}} \frac{1}{(2\pi i)^2} \int_{\sigma - i\omega_1}^{\sigma + i\omega_1} \int_{\tau - i\omega_2}^{\tau + i\omega_2} e^{px+qy} F(p, q)\, dp\, dq$$

or

$$f(x, y) = -\frac{1}{4\pi^2} \int_{\sigma - i\infty}^{\sigma + i\infty} \int_{\tau - i\infty}^{\tau + i\infty} e^{px+qy} F(p, q)\, dp\, dq, \tag{1.30}$$

where $\sigma > k_1$ and $\tau > k_2$.

Proof. Supposing $p = \sigma + i\mu$, $q = \tau + i\nu$ and taking an arbitrary point $x = a$, $y = b$ ($0 < a < \infty$, $0 < b < \infty$), we have

$$\frac{1}{(2\pi i)^2} \int_{\sigma - i\omega_1}^{\sigma + i\omega_1} \int_{\tau - i\omega_2}^{\tau + i\omega_2} e^{pa+qb} F(p, q)\, dp\, dq =$$

$$= \frac{1}{4\pi^2} \int_{-\omega_1}^{\omega_1} \int_{-\omega_2}^{\omega_2} e^{(\sigma+i\mu)a + (\tau+i\nu)b} F(\sigma + i\mu, \tau + i\nu)\, d\mu\, d\nu =$$

$$= \frac{1}{4\pi^2} \int_0^\infty \int_0^\infty f(x, y)\, dx\, dy \int_{-\omega_1}^{\omega_1} \int_{-\omega_2}^{\omega_2} e^{(\sigma+i\mu)(a-x) + (\tau+i\nu)(b-y)}\, d\mu\, d\nu =$$

$$= \frac{e^{\sigma a + \tau b}}{4\pi^2} \int_0^\infty \int_0^\infty f(x, y)\, e^{-\sigma x - \tau y} \frac{\sin \omega_1 (x - a)}{x - a} \frac{\sin \omega_2 (y - b)}{y - b}\, dx\, dy. \tag{1.31}$$

Writing

$$G(x, y) = f(x, y) - f(a, y) - f(x, b) + f(a, b),$$

it is clear that

$$G''_{xy}(x, y) = f''_{xy}(x, y) = g(x, y) \tag{1.32}$$

and

$$G(x, y) = \int_a^x \int_b^y g(u, v)\, du\, dv.$$

Hence the function

$$\varphi(x, y) = \frac{G(x, y)}{(x-a)(y-b)} \tag{1.33}$$

is continuous for all $0 < x < \infty$, $0 < y < \infty$. From (1.28) and (1.32) it follows that

$$|\varphi(x, y)| < \frac{Q}{(x-a)(y-b)} \int_a^x \int_b^y e^{k_1 u + k_2 v}\, du\, dv,$$

for all $x > a$, $y > b$, whence

$$|\varphi(x, y)| < Qe^{k_1 x + k_2 y}.$$

In the same way we find $|\varphi(x, y)| < Qe^{k_1 x + k_2 b}$ when $x > a$, $y < b$ and $|\varphi(x, y)| < Qe^{k_1 a + k_2 y}$ when $x < a$, $y > b$, and when $x \leqslant a$, $y \leqslant b$ we obtain $|\varphi(x, y)| \leqslant Qe^{k_1 a + k_2 b}$. Consequently, for all $0 < x < \infty$, $0 < y < \infty$ the inequality

$$|\varphi(x, y)| < Q_1 e^{k_1 x + k_2 y}, \tag{1.34}$$

holds, where $Q_1 = Qe^{k_1 a + k_2 b}$. Using the function $\varphi(x, y)$ we can write the equality (1.31) in the form

$$\frac{1}{(2\pi i)^2} \int_{\sigma - i\omega_1}^{\sigma + i\omega_1} \int_{\tau - i\omega_2}^{\tau + i\omega_2} e^{pa + qb} F(p, q)\, dp\, dq =$$

$$= \frac{e^{\sigma a + \tau b}}{\pi^2} \left\{ \int_0^\infty \int_0^\infty \varphi(x, y) e^{-\sigma x - \tau y} \sin \omega_1 (x-a) \sin \omega_2 (y-b)\, dx\, dy + \right.$$

$$+ \int_0^\infty \int_0^\infty f(a, y) e^{-\sigma x - \tau y} \frac{\sin \omega_1 (x-a)}{x-a} \frac{\sin \omega_2 (y-b)}{y-b}\, dx\, dy +$$

$$+\int_0^\infty\int_0^\infty f(x,\ b)\,e^{-\sigma x-\tau y}\,\frac{\sin\omega_1(x-a)}{x-a}\,\frac{\sin\omega_2(y-b)}{y-b}\,dx\,dy-$$

$$\left.-\int_0^\infty\int_0^\infty f(a,\ b)\,e^{-\sigma x-\tau y}\,\frac{\sin\omega_1(x-a)}{x-a}\,\frac{\sin\omega_2(y-b)}{y-b}\,dx\,dy\right\}. \quad (1.35)$$

Let us consider the first integral occurring on the right side of this last equation. We assume that $\sigma>k_1$, $\tau>k_2$; then it follows from the inequality (1.34) that the integral

$$\int_0^\infty\int_0^\infty|\varphi(x,\ y)|\,e^{-\sigma x-\tau y}\,dx\,dy$$

is absolutely convergent. By theorem 7 we have therefore

$$\lim_{\substack{\omega_1\to\infty\\ \omega_2\to\infty}}\int_0^\infty\int_0^\infty\varphi(x,\ y)\,e^{-\sigma x-\tau y}\sin\omega_1(x-a)\sin\omega_2(y-b)\,dx\,dy=0.$$

We apply the theory of Fourier integrals in one variable to the other three integrals. From (1.28) we see that the integrals

$$\int_0^\infty|f(x,\ b)|\,e^{-\sigma x}\,dx,\qquad\int_0^\infty|f(a,\ y)|\,e^{-\tau y}\,dy$$

exist for $\sigma>k_1$, $\tau>k_2$. We know also from the hypotheses of the theorem that the functions $f(x,\ b)$ and $f(a,\ y)$ are differentiable in x and y respectively. Therefore

$$\lim_{\omega_1\to\infty}\int_0^\infty f(x,\ b)\,e^{-\sigma x}\,\frac{\sin\omega_1(x-a)}{x-a}\,dx=\pi f(a,\ b)\,e^{-\sigma a},$$

$$\lim_{\omega_2\to\infty}\int_0^\infty e^{-\tau y}f(a,y)\,\frac{\sin\omega_2(y-b)}{y-b}\,dy=\pi f(a,\ b)\,e^{-\tau b}.$$

Also

$$\lim_{\omega_1\to\infty}\int_0^\infty e^{-\sigma x}\,\frac{\sin\omega_1(x-a)}{x-a}\,dx=\pi e^{-\sigma a},$$

$$\lim_{\omega_2\to\infty}\int_0^\infty e^{-\tau y}\,\frac{\sin\omega_2(y-b)}{y-b}\,dy=\pi e^{-\tau b}.$$

Thus the four integrals on the right side of (1.35) converge as $\omega_1 \to \infty$ and $\omega_2 \to \infty$: the first integral converges to zero and the three others converge to the same limit $\pi^2 f(a, b) e^{-\sigma a - \tau b}$. Consequently, the limit as $\omega_1 \to \infty$, $\omega_2 \to \infty$ of the left side of (1.35) exists, and

$$\lim_{\substack{\omega_1 \to \infty \\ \omega_2 \to \infty}} \frac{1}{(2\pi i)^2} \int_{\sigma - i\omega_1}^{\sigma + i\omega_1} \int_{\tau - i\omega_2}^{\tau + i\omega_2} e^{pa+qb} F(p, q)\, dp\, dq = f(a, b) \quad (1.36)$$

which was to be proved.

Formula (1.36) has been proved on the assumption that $a > 0$, $b > 0$. If $a < 0$, $b < 0$, it follows immediately from (1.31) that the limit in (1.36) is equal to zero. When either $a < 0$, $b > 0$ or $a > 0, b < 0$, it is obvious from the proof that the limit in (1.36) is again equal to zero. Lastly, when $a = 0$, $b > 0$; $a > 0$, $b = 0$ or $a = 0$, $b = 0$, then the desired limit will be equal to $\frac{1}{2} f(+0, b)$; $\frac{1}{2} f(a, +0)$; $\frac{1}{4} [f(0, +0) + f(+0, 0) - f(0, 0)]$ respectively.

Remark. For the existence of the limits as $\omega_1 \to \infty$ and $\omega_2 \to \infty$ of the last three integrals on the right side of (1.35) it is sufficient that the function $f(x, y)$ satisfies separately in each of the variables the conditions guaranteeing the inversion theorem for the case of one variable. For example, it is sufficient that the functions $\varphi(x) = f(x, y)$ (y fixed and arbitrary) and $\psi(y) = f(x, y)$ (x fixed and arbitrary) be functions of bounded variation in the neighbourhood of any point, and that the integrals

$$\int_0^\infty e^{-\sigma x} |\varphi(x)|\, dx, \quad \int_0^\infty e^{-\tau y} |\psi(y)|\, dy$$

converge. If these conditions are satisfied the proof of the inversion theorem reduces to the study of the limiting behaviour of the integral

$$\int_0^\infty \int_0^\infty \varphi(x, y) e^{-\sigma x - \tau y} \sin \omega_1 (x - a) \sin \omega_2 (y - b)\, dx\, dy \quad (1.37)$$

as $\omega_1 \to \infty$, $\omega_2 \to \infty$.

For this purpose we divide the region of integration in (1.37) into the set defined by the inequalities $|x - a| \geqslant \delta$, $|y - b| \geqslant \varepsilon$ and its complement which we shall denote by $R(\varepsilon, \delta)$. To prove that the integral (1.37) tends to zero as $\omega_1 \to \infty, \omega_2 \to \infty$ it is clearly sufficient to show that

$$\lim_{\substack{\varepsilon \to \infty \\ \delta \to \infty}} \iint_{R(\varepsilon, \delta)} |\varphi(x, y)| e^{-\sigma x - \tau y} \, dx \, dy = 0.$$

Because

$$\iint_{R(\varepsilon, \delta)} |\varphi(x, y)| e^{-\sigma x - \tau y} \, dx \, dy \leqslant \int_{a-\delta}^{a+\delta} dx \int_0^\infty |\varphi(x, y)| e^{-\sigma x - \tau y} dy + \int_{b-\varepsilon}^{b+\varepsilon} dy \int_0^\infty |\varphi(x, y)| e^{-\sigma x - \tau y} \, dx,$$

we need only consider the behaviour of the integrals

$$\left.\begin{array}{l} \int_{a-\delta}^{a+\delta} dx \int_0^\infty |\varphi(x, y)| e^{-\tau y} \, dy, \\ \int_{b-\varepsilon}^{b+\varepsilon} dy \int_0^\infty |\varphi(x, y)| e^{-\sigma x} \, dx \end{array}\right\} \tag{1.38}$$

as $\delta \to \infty$ and $\varepsilon \to \infty$. If the function $f(x, y)$ satisfies the conditions

$$|f(x, y) - f(a, y)| \leqslant M |x - a|^\alpha e^{k_1 x + k_2 y},$$
$$|f(x, y) - f(x, b)| \leqslant M |y - b|^\alpha e^{k_1 x + k_2 y}$$

(where M and α are positive constants independent of the numbers a and b) then

$$|G(x, y)| \leqslant M |x - a|^\alpha e^{k_1 x + k_2 y},$$
$$|G(x, y)| \leqslant M |y - b|^\alpha e^{k_1 x + k_2 y},$$

or

$$|G(x, y)| \leqslant M |x - a|^{\frac{\alpha}{2}} |y - b|^{\frac{\alpha}{2}} e^{k_1 x + k_2 y}.$$

Consequently

$$|\varphi(x, y)| \leqslant M |x - a|^{\frac{\alpha}{2} - 1} |y - b|^{\frac{\alpha}{2} - 1} e^{k_1 x + k_2 y}.$$

Therefore

$$\left|\int_{a-\delta}^{a+\delta} dx \int_{0}^{\infty} |\varphi(x, y)| e^{-\tau y} dy\right| \leqslant$$

$$\leqslant \left|M \int_{a-\delta}^{a+\delta} e^{k_1 x} |x-a|^{\frac{\alpha}{2}-1} dx \int_{0}^{\infty} e^{-(\tau-k_2)y} |y-b|^{\frac{\alpha}{2}-1} dy\right|.$$

If $\alpha > 0$, it is clear that

$$\lim_{\delta\to\infty} \int_{a-\delta}^{a+\delta} dx \int_{0}^{\infty} |\varphi(x, y)| e^{-\tau y} dy = 0.$$

In the same way we obtain

$$\lim_{\varepsilon\to\infty} \int_{b-\varepsilon}^{b+\varepsilon} dy \int_{0}^{\infty} |\varphi(x, y)| e^{-\sigma x} dx = 0,$$

and the proof is complete.

CHAPTER 2

BASIC DEFINITIONS AND THEOREMS OF THE OPERATIONAL CALCULUS IN TWO VARIABLES AND ITS APPLICATIONS

Although the operational calculus has recently been considerably generalized (see, for example, the works of Mikusinskii [6] and Schwartz [54]), it is often expedient in practical problems to make use of the operational calculus based on the application of the Laplace transform. We therefore direct our attention to constructing the apparatus of an operational calculus in two variables on this basis. Instead of the Laplace transform we shall study the Laplace-Carson transform

$$F(p,\ q) = pq\int_0^\infty\int_0^\infty e^{-px-qy} f(x,\ y)\,dx\,dy, \qquad (2.1)$$

and we shall write $F(p,\ q) \mathrel{\overset{\cdot\cdot}{\underset{\cdot\cdot}{=}}} f(x,\ y)$ by analogy with the one-dimensional symbolism $F(p) \mathrel{\dot{=}} f(x)$. We shall call the function $F(p,\ q)$ the <u>image</u>, and the function $f(x,\ y)$ the <u>original.</u> Thus the unit function $\eta(x,\ y)$ * transforms into itself, i.e. $\eta(p,\ q) = 1$. Because the Laplace-Carson transform differs from the Laplace transform only in the factor pq, it is clear that all the theorems and properties of the Laplace transform can be reformulated for the Laplace-Carson transform. In what follows we shall denote the original variables by x and y and the transformed variables by p and q. In addition, we shall use the notations

$$F_1(p,\ y) = p\int_0^\infty e^{-p\xi} f(\xi,\ y)\,d\xi; \quad F_2(x,\ q) = q\int_0^\infty e^{-q\eta} f(x,\eta)\,d\eta$$

for the intermediate transforms of the function $f(x,\ y)$ with respect to one of the variables.

---

* This is the function which is equal to 1 when both x and y are positive, and is equal to zero when at least one of the arguments is negative.

1. The Similarity Rule and the Shift Rule

The Similarity Rule. If $F(p, q) \doteqdot f(x, y)$, then

$$F\left(\frac{p}{a}, \frac{q}{b}\right) \doteqdot f(ax, by), \tag{2.2}$$

where a and b are positive numbers, and $f(x, y)$ is a function of real variables defined for positive values of x and y and belonging to the class S.

The Shift Rule for an Image. If $F(p, q) \doteqdot f(x, y)$, then

$$\frac{p}{p+a}\frac{q}{q+b}F(p+a, q+b) \doteqdot e^{-ax-by} f(x, y) \tag{2.3}$$

for arbitrary a and b.

The Shift Rule for an Original. In contrast to the preceding rule the original of $e^{-ap-bq}F(p, q)$ exists only for real and positive values of a and b. Then, if $F(p, q) \doteqdot f(x, y)$, we have

$$e^{-ap-bq}F(p, q) \doteqdot \begin{cases} 0 & \text{for } x < a \text{ or } y < b, \\ f(x-a, y-b) & \text{for } x > a, y > b. \end{cases} \tag{2.4}$$

2. The Images of Integrals and Derivatives. The Multiplication Rule

The Image of Integrals. If $F(p, q) \doteqdot f(x, y)$, we have the following relations

$$\int_0^x f(\xi, y)\, d\xi \doteqdot \frac{1}{p} F(p, q), \tag{2.5}$$

$$\int_0^y f(x, \eta)\, d\eta \doteqdot \frac{1}{q} F(p, q), \tag{2.6}$$

$$\int_0^x \int_0^y f(\xi, \eta)\, d\xi\, d\eta \doteqdot \frac{1}{pq} F(p, q), \tag{2.7}$$

$$\int_x^{\infty} \frac{f(\xi, y)}{\xi} d\xi \risingdotseq \int_0^{p} \frac{F(\xi, q)}{\xi} d\xi, \tag{2.8}$$

$$\int_y^{\infty} \frac{f(x, \eta)}{\eta} d\eta \risingdotseq \int_0^{q} \frac{F(p, \eta)}{\eta} d\eta, \tag{2.9}$$

$$\int_x^{\infty}\int_y^{\infty} \frac{f(\xi, \eta)}{\xi\eta} d\xi\, d\eta \risingdotseq \int_0^{p}\int_0^{q} \frac{F(\xi, \eta)}{\xi\eta} d\xi\, d\eta, \tag{2.10}$$

$$\int_0^{x} \frac{f(\xi, y)}{\xi} d\xi \risingdotseq \int_p^{\infty} \frac{F(\xi, q)}{\xi} d\xi, \tag{2.11}$$

$$\int_0^{y} \frac{f(x, \eta)}{\eta} d\eta \risingdotseq \int_q^{\infty} \frac{F(p, \eta)}{\eta} d\eta, \tag{2.12}$$

$$\int_0^{x}\int_0^{y} \frac{f(\xi, \eta)}{\xi\eta} d\xi\, d\eta \risingdotseq \int_p^{\infty}\int_q^{\infty} \frac{F(\xi, \eta)}{\xi\eta} d\xi\, d\eta. \tag{2.13}$$

We assume that all the improper integrals in (2.5) to (2.13) converge. Similar relations may be derived for integrals of higher multiplicity.

The Image of Derivatives. The existence of the image of a function does not imply the existence of images of its derivatives. However, if these images exist, then they can be found in the same way as in the one-dimensional case, only here we need to know a greater number of initial values. As an example we shall find the original of the function $pF(p, q)$. Integrating by parts we obtain

$$pF(p, q) = pq \int_0^{\infty} e^{-qy} \left\{ -e^{-px} f(x, y) \Big|_{x=0}^{x=\infty} \right\} dy +$$
$$+ pq \int_0^{\infty}\int_0^{\infty} e^{-px-qy} \frac{\partial f(x, y)}{\partial x} dx\, dy,$$

and if $f(0, y) = 0$ for all $y > 0$ it follows that

$$pF(p, q) \risingdotseq \frac{\partial f(x, y)}{\partial x}.$$

In the same way, if $f(x, 0) = 0$, for all $x > 0$,

$$qF(p, q) \doteqdot \frac{\partial f(x, y)}{\partial y}.$$

Let $f(0, y) = f_1(y) \doteq F_1(q)$; then

$$f(x, y) - f_1(y) \doteqdot F(p, q) - F_1(q).$$

Differentiating this symbolic equation with respect to x we derive

$$\frac{\partial f(x, y)}{\partial x} \doteqdot p[F(p, q) - F_1(q)].$$

Similarly, if $f(x, 0) = f_2(x) \doteq F_2(p)$,

$$\frac{\partial f(x, y)}{\partial y} \doteqdot q[F(p, q) - F_2(p)].$$

Differentiating the operational relation

$$f(x, y) - f_1(y) - f_2(x) + \\ + f(0, 0) \doteqdot F(p, q) - F_1(q) - F_2(p) + f(0, 0)$$

with respect to x and y we obtain

$$\frac{\partial f(x, y)}{\partial x} - \frac{\partial f_2(x)}{\partial x} \doteqdot p[F(p, q) - F_1(q) - F_2(p) + f(0, 0)],$$

$$\frac{\partial f(x, y)}{\partial y} - \frac{\partial f_1(y)}{\partial y} \doteqdot q[F(p, q) - F_1(q) - F_2(p) + f(0, 0)],$$

$$\frac{\partial^2 f(x, y)}{\partial x\, \partial y} \doteqdot pq[F(p, q) - F_1(q) - F_2(p) + f(0, 0)].$$

We can deduce more operational relations involving derivatives by differentiating with respect to a parameter. For example, if we differentiate the symbolic equation

$$f(ax, by) \doteqdot F\left(\frac{p}{a}, \frac{q}{b}\right)$$

several times with respect to a and b and if we then set $a = b = 1$, we find

$$x\frac{\partial f(x, y)}{\partial x} \doteqdot -p\frac{\partial F(p, q)}{\partial p},$$

$$xy\frac{\partial^2 f(x, y)}{\partial x\, dy} \doteqdot pq\frac{\partial^2 F(p, q)}{\partial p\, \partial q}$$

etc. We have assumed that the function $f(x, y)$ is differentiable in the entire region of definition and that the image functions of the derivatives exist. We may generalize these last two formulæ:

$$x^n y^m \frac{\partial^{m+n} f(x, y)}{\partial x^n \partial y^m} \doteqdot (-1)^{m+n} \frac{\partial^{m+n-2}}{\partial p^{n-1} \partial q^{m-1}} \left[p^n q^m \frac{\partial^2 F(p, q)}{\partial p \, \partial q} \right],$$

$$x^r y^s \frac{\partial^{m+n} f(x, y)}{\partial x^n \partial y^m} \doteqdot (-1)^{r+s} pq \frac{\partial^{r+s}}{\partial p^r \partial q^s} [p^{n-1} q^{m-1} F(p, q)],$$

where $r \geqslant m$, $s \geqslant n$ (r, s, m, n positive integers). In addition

$$\frac{\partial^{r+s-2}}{\partial x^{r-1} \partial y^{s-1}} \left[x^n y^m \frac{\partial^2 f(x, y)}{\partial x \, \partial y} \right] \doteqdot (-1)^{m+n} p^r q^s \frac{\partial^{m+n} F(p,q)}{\partial p^n \partial q^m},$$

with $m \geqslant r$, $n \geqslant s$ (r, s, m, n positive integers). These formulæ are often applied in the solution of partial differential equations.

The Multiplication Rule. If $F_1(p, q) \doteqdot f_1(x, y)$ and $F_2(p, q) \doteqdot f_2(x, y)$, we have the following operational relation (see Theorem 12 above), which is very useful in applications:

$$f_1(x, y) \overset{x\, y}{**} f_2(x, y) \doteqdot \frac{1}{pq} F_1(p, q) F_2(p, q), \tag{2.14}$$

where

$$f_1(x, y) \overset{x\, y}{**} f_2(x, y) = \int_0^x \int_0^y f_1(\xi, \eta) f_2(x - \xi, y - \eta) \, d\xi \, d\eta.$$

The double asterisk denotes the double convolution with respect to x and y. We shall also need the convolution with respect to x alone

$$f_1(x, y) \overset{x}{*} f_2(x, y) = \int_0^x f_1(\xi, y) f_2(x - \xi, y) \, d\xi,$$

and y alone

$$f_1(x, y) \overset{y}{*} f_2(x, y) = \int_0^y f_1(x, \eta) f_2(x, y - \eta) \, d\eta.$$

3. Linear Combinations of the Variables p and q

Let m and M be the smaller and the larger of the values x and y respectively, and suppose that the Laplace transform of the function $f(x)$ exists. We shall evaluate the transform of the function $f(m)$, i.e.

$$F(p, q) = pq \int_0^\infty \int_0^\infty e^{-px-qy} f(m) \, dx \, dy.$$

We divide the first quadrant of the $x\ y$ -plane by the line $x=y$ $f(m)=f(y)$ in the region $x>y$ and $f(m)=f(x)$ in the region $x<y$ so that we have

$$F(p, q)=pq\int_0^\infty e^{-qy} f(y)\, dy \int_y^\infty e^{-px}\, dx + pq \int_0^\infty e^{-px} f(x)\, dx \times$$

$$\times \int_x^\infty e^{-qy}\, dy=(p+q)\int_0^\infty e^{-(p+q)u} f(u)\, du=F(p+q),$$

i.e.

$$f(m) \doteqdot F(p+q), \tag{2.15}$$

where

$$F(p)=p\int_0^\infty e^{-px} f(x)\, dx.$$

In the same way we derive the following operational relations:

$$f(M) \doteqdot F(p)+F(q)-F(p+q), \tag{2.16}$$

$$\left.\begin{matrix} f(x) & \text{for} & x<y \\ 0 & \text{for} & x>y \end{matrix}\right\} \doteqdot \frac{p}{p+q} F(p+q), \tag{2.17}$$

$$\left.\begin{matrix} f(x) & \text{for} & x<y \\ f_1(y) & \text{for} & x>y \end{matrix}\right\} \doteqdot \frac{pF(p+q)+qF_1(p+q)}{p+q}, \tag{2.18}$$

where

$$F_1(q)=q\int_0^\infty e^{-qy} f_1(y)\, dy;$$

$$\left.\begin{matrix} f(y) & \text{for} & x<y \\ f_1(x) & \text{for} & x>y \end{matrix}\right\} \doteqdot F(q)+F_1(p)-\frac{qF(p+q)+pF_1(p+q)}{p+q}, \tag{2.19}$$

$$\left.\begin{matrix} f(x)(y-x)^\nu & \text{for} & y>x \\ 0 & \text{for} & y<x \end{matrix}\right\} \doteqdot \frac{\Gamma(\nu+1)\, pF(p+q)}{q^\nu (p+q)}, \tag{2.20}$$

$$\left.\begin{matrix} f(x) & \text{for} & y<ax;\ y>bx \\ 0 & & \text{otherwise} \\ & & a>b \end{matrix}\right\} \doteqdot F(p)-\frac{p}{p+aq} F(p+aq)+ + \frac{p}{p+bq} F(p+bq). \tag{2.21}$$

We find now the original of the function $\frac{F(p, q)}{p+q}$, which occurs often in the solution of partial differential equations.

Let

$$F(p, q) \doteqdot F_1(x, q) \doteqdot f(x, y).$$

Because

$$\frac{p}{p+q} \doteqdot e^{-qx},$$

we invoke the multiplication rule to obtain

$$\frac{F(p, q)}{p+q} = \frac{1}{p}\frac{p}{p+q}F(p, q) \doteqdot e^{-qx} \overset{x}{*} F_1(x, q) = \\ = \int_0^x e^{-q\xi} F_1(x-\xi, q)\, d\xi.$$

Applying the shift rule to the variable q, we have

$$e^{-q\xi}F_1(x-\xi, q) \doteqdot \begin{cases} 0 & \text{for} \quad y < \xi, \\ f(x-\xi, y-\xi) & \text{for} \quad y > \xi, \end{cases}$$

from which it follows that

$$\frac{F(p, q)}{p+q} \doteqdot \int_0^{\min(x, y)} f(x-\xi, y-\xi)\, d\xi. \tag{2.22}$$

In particular

$$\frac{F(p)\, F_1(q)}{p+q} \doteqdot \int_0^{\min(x, y)} f(x-\xi) f_1(y-\xi)\, d\xi. \tag{2.23}$$

Let us consider the integral

$$\frac{F(ap+bq, a_1p+b_1q)}{(ap+bq)(a_1p+b_1q)} = \int_0^\infty \int_0^\infty e^{-(ap+bq)\xi-(a_1p+b_1q)\eta} f(\xi, \eta)\, d\xi\, d\eta.$$

where a, b, a_1, b_1 are non-negative real numbers, such that $\Delta = ab_1 - a_1b \neq 0$. We make the change of variables

$$a\xi + a_1\eta = x, \quad b\xi + b_1\eta = y.$$

Then

$$pq\frac{F(ap+bq,\ a_1p+b_1q)}{(ap+bq)(a_1p+b_1q)} \risingdotseq \frac{1}{\Delta} f\left(\frac{b_1x-a_1y}{\Delta},\quad \frac{ay-bx}{\Delta}\right), \tag{2.24}$$

where we define $f(x, y)$ to be zero whenever one of its arguments is negative. In particular we have

$$\frac{p}{p+q}F(p+q,\ q) \risingdotseq \begin{cases} f(x,\ y-x) & \text{for} \quad y > x, \\ 0 & \text{for} \quad y < x, \end{cases}$$

which is a generalization of formula (2.17).

4. Functions of Functions

We shall suppose

$$F(p) = p\int_0^\infty e^{-ps} f(s)\,ds \tag{2.25}$$

and we shall assume the validity of the operational relations

$$\alpha(p)\,e^{-s\rho(p)} \doteqdot A(x,\ s),$$
$$\beta(q)\,e^{-s\sigma(q)} \doteqdot B(y,\ s).$$

Writing $\rho(p)+\sigma(q)$ for p in (2.25) we derive

$$\frac{\alpha(p)\,\beta(q)\,F[\rho(p)+\sigma(q)]}{\rho(p)+\sigma(q)} \risingdotseq \int_0^\infty A(x,\ s)\,B(y,\ s)\,f(s)\,ds. \tag{2.26}$$

We give some examples of relations derived in this way:

$$\frac{pqF(\sqrt{p^2+1}+\sqrt{q^2+1})}{\sqrt{p^2+1}\sqrt{q^2+1}\,[\sqrt{p^2+1}+\sqrt{q^2+1}} \risingdotseq \int_0^m J_0\left(2\sqrt{x^2-s^2}\right) \times$$
$$\times J_0\left(2\sqrt{y^2-s^2}\right) f(s)\,ds, \tag{2.27}$$

$$F_1(p)\,F_2(q)\frac{F(p+q)}{p+q} \risingdotseq \int_0^m f_1(x-s)\,f_2(y-s)\,f(s)\,ds, \tag{2.28}$$

$$\frac{F(p+\ln q)}{p+\ln q} \risingdotseq \int_0^x \frac{y^s f(s)\,ds}{\Gamma(1+s)}. \tag{2.29}$$

Starting from the integral (2.1) an expression similar to (2.26) can be derived analogously. The formulae derived here allow us to represent in the form of double integrals the originals of images which are functions of functions, and this has important applications in the solution of partial differential equations. For example, we have

$$\frac{pqF(\sqrt{p^2+1},\ \sqrt{q^2+1})}{(p^2+1)(q^2+1)} \doteqdot \int_0^x \int_0^y J_0\left(\sqrt{x^2-\xi^2}\right) J_0\left(\sqrt{y^2-\eta^2}\right) \times \times f(\xi,\ \eta)\, d\xi\, d\eta,$$

$$\frac{pqF\left(p+\frac{1}{p},\ q+\frac{1}{q}\right)}{(p^2+1)(q^2+1)} \doteqdot \int_0^x \int_0^y J_0\left(2\sqrt{\xi(x-\xi)}\right) \times \times J_0\left(2\sqrt{\eta(y-\eta)}\right) f(\xi,\ \eta)\, d\xi\, d\eta.$$

Finally, we remark that we may need to find the originals of image functions such as $F(p,\ p)$, $F\left(\sqrt{p},\ p\right)$ etc. For example, let us find the original of $F(p,\ p)$. We write

$$\frac{1}{p} F(p,\ p) = p \int_0^\infty \int_0^\infty e^{-p(\xi+\eta)} f(\xi,\ \eta)\, d\xi\, d\eta.$$

If we introduce the new variable $x = \xi + \eta$ we will have

$$\frac{1}{p} F(p,\ p) = p \int_0^\infty e^{-px}\, dx \int_0^x f(\xi,\ x-\xi)\, d\xi,$$

i.e.

$$\frac{1}{p} F(p,\ p) \doteqdot \int_0^x f(\xi,\ x-\xi)\, d\xi = \int_0^x f(x-\xi,\ \xi)\, d\xi. \quad (2.30)$$

5. The Image of the Function $f(x+y)$

Let $F(p) \doteqdot f(x)$. We shall evaluate the image of the function $f(x+y)$. Making the change of variable $x+y=u$, we obtain

$$F(p,\ q) = pq \int_0^\infty \int_0^\infty e^{-px-qy} f(x+y)\, dx\, dy =$$

$$= pq \int_0^\infty e^{-pu} f(u)\, du \int_0^u e^{(p-q)y}\, dy =$$

$$= \frac{pq}{p-q} \int_0^\infty (e^{-qu} - e^{-pu}) f(u)\, du = \frac{pF(q) - qF(p)}{p-q},$$

i.e.

$$f(x+y) \doteqdot \frac{pF(q) - qF(p)}{p-q}. \tag{2.31}$$

For example,

$$\sin(x+y) \doteqdot \frac{pq(p+q)}{(p^2+1)(q^2+1)},$$

$$\cos(x+y) \doteqdot \frac{pq(pq-1)}{(p^2+1)(q^2+1)},$$

$$J_0(2\sqrt{x+y}) \doteqdot \frac{qe^{-\frac{1}{p}} - pe^{-\frac{1}{q}}}{q-p}.$$

In the same way we find for the derivative and integral of $f(x)$

$$f'(x+y) \doteqdot pq \frac{F(q) - F(p)}{p-q}, \tag{2.32}$$

$$\int_0^x f(\xi)\, d\xi + \int_0^y f(\xi)\, d\xi - \int_0^{x+y} f(\xi)\, d\xi \doteqdot \frac{F(p) - F(q)}{p-q}. \tag{2.33}$$

We shall derive now the image of the function $(x+y)^m$. We could make use of (2.31), but it follows immediately from

$$(x+y)^m = \sum_{n=0}^{m} \frac{m(m-1)\dots(m-n+1)}{n!} x^n y^{m-n}$$

that

$$(x+y)^m \doteqdot \sum_{n=0}^{m} \frac{m(m-1)\dots(m-n-1)}{n!} \frac{n!(m-n)!}{p^n q^{m-n}}$$

or

$$(x+y)^m \doteqdot \sum_{n=0}^{m} \frac{m!}{p^n q^{m-n}} = \frac{m!}{q^m} \sum_{n=0}^{m} \left(\frac{q}{p}\right)^n,$$

and therefore

$$(x+y)^m \doteqdot \frac{m!}{p^m q^m} \frac{q^{m+1} - p^{m+1}}{q-p}. \tag{2.34}$$

Differentiating this last symbolic expression with respect to m and then putting $m=0$, we obtain the relation

$$\ln(x+y) \doteqdot \frac{p\ln q - q\ln p}{q-p} - C, \tag{2.35}$$

where C is Euler's constant.

Applying the similarity rule to (2.31) we derive

$$f(ax+by) \doteqdot \frac{bpF\left(\frac{q}{b}\right) - aqF\left(\frac{p}{a}\right)}{bp-aq}. \tag{2.36}$$

As before, the numbers a and b must be real and positive.

6. The Image of the Function $f(|x-y|)$

If we define $f(x)$ to be zero for negative values of the argument, we can find the image of the function $f(x-y)$. If we write

$$f_1(x, y) = \begin{cases} f(x-y) & \text{for} \quad x > y, \\ 0 & \text{for} \quad x < y, \end{cases}$$

we have

$$F_1(p, q) = pq\int_0^\infty e^{-qy}\,dy \int_y^\infty e^{-px} f(x-y)\,dx.$$

Setting $x-y=u$, we obtain

$$f_1(x, y) \doteqdot F_1(p, q) = \frac{q}{p+q} F(p). \tag{2.37}$$

In the same way we find the image of the function

$$f_2(x, y) = \begin{cases} f(y-x) & \text{for} \quad y > x, \\ 0 & \text{for} \quad y < x, \end{cases}$$

which has the form (by symmetry with (2.37))

$$f_2(x, y) \doteqdot F_2(p, q) = \frac{p}{p+q} F(q). \tag{2.38}$$

Adding (2.37) and (2.38) we get

$$f_1(x, y) + f_2(x, y) = f(|x-y|) \doteqdot \frac{pF(q) + qF(p)}{p+q}.$$

7. The Image of the Function $f(xy)$

We shall make use of the integral

$$\int_0^\infty e^{-pt-\frac{q}{t}}\frac{dt}{t}=2K_0(2\sqrt{pq}).$$

Then

$$\int_0^\infty\int_0^\infty e^{-px-qy}f(xy)\,dx\,dy=$$

$$=\int_0^\infty\frac{e^{-px}}{x}dx\int_0^\infty e^{-\frac{q\xi}{x}}f(\xi)\,d\xi=2\int_0^\infty K_0(2\sqrt{pq\xi})f(\xi)d\xi,$$

so that

$$f(xy)\doteqdot 2pq\int_0^\infty K_0(2\sqrt{pq\xi})f(\xi)\,d\xi. \qquad (2.39)$$

8. The Image of the Function $Ji_0(2\sqrt{xy})$

We are concerned here with the function

$$Ji_0(x)=\int_x^\infty\frac{J_0(u)}{u}du;$$

we have

$$-Ji_0(2\sqrt{x})=C+\ln\sqrt{x}+\sum_{s=1}^\infty\frac{(-1)^s x^s}{s!s!2s}.$$

Because

$$\ln\left(1+\frac{1}{pq}\right)=-\sum_{s=1}^\infty\frac{(-1)^s}{sp^sq^s}\doteqdot-\sum_{s=1}^\infty\frac{(-1)^s x^s y^s}{s!s!s},$$

then

$$\ln\left(1+\frac{1}{pq}\right)\doteqdot 2Ji_0(2\sqrt{xy})+2C+\ln xy;$$

and since

$$\ln pq\doteqdot -2C-\ln xy,$$

$$\ln\left(1+\frac{1}{pq}\right)\doteqdot 2Ji_0(2\sqrt{xy})+2C+\ln xy;$$

it follows that

$$\ln(pq+1) \doteqdot 2Ji_0\left(2\sqrt{xy}\right).$$

9. The Image of the Function $\frac{1}{\sqrt{\pi(x+y)}} f\left(\frac{xy}{x+y}\right)$

Let $f(x) \doteq F(p)$. Replace p by $\sqrt{p}+\sqrt{q}$ (it will always be understood that $\sqrt{p}$ and $\sqrt{q}$ are on that branch for which $\sqrt{1}=1$, $\arg 1 = 0$), then

$$\sqrt{pq}\frac{F(\sqrt{p}+\sqrt{q})}{\sqrt{p}+\sqrt{q}} = \int_0^\infty \sqrt{p}\, e^{-\xi\sqrt{p}} \sqrt{q}\, e^{-\xi\sqrt{q}} f(\xi)\, d\xi.$$

Since

$$\sqrt{p}\cdot e^{-\xi\sqrt{p}} \doteq \frac{e^{-\frac{\xi^2}{4x}}}{\sqrt{\pi x}},$$

we deduce that

$$\sqrt{pq}\frac{F(\sqrt{p}+\sqrt{q})}{\sqrt{p}+\sqrt{q}} \doteqdot \int_0^\infty \frac{e^{-\xi^2\frac{x+y}{4xy}}}{\pi\sqrt{xy}} f(\xi)\, d\xi. \qquad (2.40)$$

We put $\xi = \sqrt{u}$ in (2.40); then

$$\sqrt{pq}\frac{F(\sqrt{p}+\sqrt{q})}{\sqrt{p}+\sqrt{q}} \doteqdot \int_0^\infty \frac{1}{2\pi\sqrt{xy}}\, e^{-u\left(\frac{x+y}{4xy}\right)} \frac{f(\sqrt{u})}{\sqrt{u}}\, du. \qquad (2.41)$$

Writing $p = \frac{x+y}{4xy}$, $f(x) \doteq F(p)$, $\frac{f(\sqrt{x})}{\sqrt{x}} \doteq G(p)$, (2.41) becomes

$$\sqrt{pq}\frac{F(\sqrt{p}+\sqrt{q})}{\sqrt{p}+\sqrt{q}} \doteqdot \frac{2\sqrt{xy}}{\pi(x+y)}\, G\left(\frac{x+y}{4xy}\right). \qquad (2.42)$$

Example. Let

$$\ln\left(1+\frac{1}{pq}\right) = -\sum_{s=1}^{\infty}\frac{(-1)^s}{sp^sq^s} \doteqdot -\sum_{s=1}^{\infty}\frac{(-1)^s x^s y^s}{s!s!s},$$

Then from (2.42) we have

$$\frac{\sqrt{pq}(\sqrt{p}+\sqrt{q})}{[(\sqrt{p}+\sqrt{q})^2+1]^{3/2}} \doteqdot \frac{2}{\pi}\frac{\sqrt{xy}}{(x+y)}e^{-\frac{xy}{x+y}}.$$

On the other hand. let us write $F(p) \doteqdot f(x)$, $F(\sqrt{p}) \doteqdot h(x)$. Then since $\frac{f(\sqrt{x})}{\sqrt{x}} \doteqdot \sqrt{p\pi}\, h\left(\frac{1}{4p}\right)$, it follows from (2.42) that

$$\sqrt{pq}\frac{F(\sqrt{p}+\sqrt{q})}{\sqrt{p}+\sqrt{q}} \doteqdot \frac{1}{\sqrt{\pi(x+y)}}\, h\left(\frac{xy}{x+y}\right). \quad (2.43)$$

This formula can be written in the alternative form

$$\sqrt{pq}\frac{F[(\sqrt{p}+\sqrt{q})^2]}{\sqrt{p}+\sqrt{q}} \doteqdot \frac{1}{\sqrt{\pi(x+y)}} f\left(\frac{xy}{x+y}\right).$$

Several other operational relations may be derived with the help of this last formula.

Starting from the formula $\cos x \doteqdot \frac{p^2}{p^2+1}$, we find

$$\sqrt{pq}\frac{(\sqrt{p}+\sqrt{q})^3}{(\sqrt{p}+\sqrt{q})^4+1} \doteqdot \frac{1}{\sqrt{\pi(x+y)}}\cos\left(\frac{xy}{x+y}\right).$$

Similarly the relation $\sin x \doteqdot \frac{p}{p^2+1}$, gives

$$\sqrt{pq}\frac{(\sqrt{p}+\sqrt{q})}{(\sqrt{p}+\sqrt{q})^4+1} \doteqdot \frac{1}{\sqrt{\pi(x+y)}}\sin\frac{xy}{x+y},$$

and from $\frac{x^{\frac{\nu}{2}}}{\Gamma\left(\frac{\nu}{2}+1\right)} \doteqdot \frac{1}{p^{\frac{\nu}{2}}}$ $(\nu > -2)$, we derive

$$\frac{\sqrt{pq}}{(\sqrt{p}+\sqrt{q})^{\nu+1}} \doteqdot \frac{(xy)^{\frac{\nu}{2}}}{\sqrt{\pi}\,\Gamma\left(\frac{\nu}{2}+1\right)(x+y)^{\frac{\nu+1}{2}}}.$$

We shall derive several more analogous formulae:

a). Let us suppose $F(p) \doteqdot f(x)$ and $f(\sqrt{x}) \doteqdot G(p)$.

Then we can find the following relations:

$$p\sqrt{q}\frac{F(\sqrt{p}+\sqrt{q})}{\sqrt{p}+\sqrt{q}} \doteqdot \frac{y}{\pi\sqrt{xy}(x+y)}\, G\left(\frac{x+y}{4xy}\right),$$

$$q\sqrt{p}\frac{F(\sqrt{p}+\sqrt{q})}{\sqrt{p}+\sqrt{q}} \doteqdot \frac{x}{\pi\sqrt{xy}\,(x+y)}\, G\left(\frac{x+y}{4xy}\right)$$

and

$$\sqrt{pq}\,F(\sqrt{p}+\sqrt{q}) \risingdotseq \frac{1}{\pi\sqrt{xy}}\,G\left(\frac{x+y}{4xy}\right).$$

Example. If $f(x)=J_0(x)\doteq\frac{p}{\sqrt{p^2+1}}$ and $J_0(\sqrt{x})\doteq e^{-\frac{1}{4p}}$, we derive

$$\frac{\sqrt{pq}\,(\sqrt{p}+\sqrt{q})}{\sqrt{1+(\sqrt{p}+\sqrt{q})^2}} \risingdotseq \frac{1}{\pi\sqrt{xy}}\,e^{-\frac{xy}{x+y}}.$$

b). Let us suppose that $f(x)\doteq F(p)$ and $\sqrt{x}\,f(\sqrt{x})\doteq\Phi(p)$: we shall derive a relation analogous to (2.42). Indeed,

$$\frac{F(\sqrt{p}+\sqrt{q})}{\sqrt{p}+\sqrt{q}}=\int_0^\infty \frac{e^{-s\sqrt{p}-s\sqrt{q}}}{s^2}\,s^2 f(s)\,ds,$$

and

$$\frac{pe^{-s\sqrt{p}}}{s}\doteq\frac{e^{-\frac{s^2}{4x}}}{2\sqrt{\pi}}\,x^{-\frac{3}{2}},\quad \frac{qe^{-s\sqrt{q}}}{s}\doteq\frac{e^{-\frac{s^2}{4y}}}{2\sqrt{\pi}}\,y^{-\frac{3}{2}}.$$

so that, after making the obvious transformations, we have

$$pq\,\frac{F(\sqrt{p}+\sqrt{q})}{\sqrt{p}+\sqrt{q}} \risingdotseq \frac{1}{8\pi}\int_0^\infty e^{-\frac{x+y}{4xy}u}\,\frac{\sqrt{u}\,f(\sqrt{u})}{(xy)^{3/2}}\,du.$$

Recalling that $\sqrt{x}\,f(\sqrt{x})\doteq\Phi(p)$, we obtain finally

$$pq\,\frac{F(\sqrt{p}+\sqrt{q})}{\sqrt{p}+\sqrt{q}} \risingdotseq \frac{1}{2\pi(x+y)\sqrt{xy}}\,\Phi\left(\frac{x+y}{4xy}\right).$$

c). Let us suppose $f(x)\doteq F(p)$ and $G(\sqrt{p})\doteq\Phi(x)$, where

$$G(p)=p\,\frac{d^2}{dp^2}\left[\frac{F(p)}{p}\right];$$

then, making use of the last relationship in the form

$$pq\,\frac{F(\sqrt{p}+\sqrt{q})}{\sqrt{p}+\sqrt{q}} \risingdotseq \frac{1}{4\pi}\int_0^\infty e^{-\frac{s^2}{4}\left(\frac{1}{x}+\frac{1}{y}\right)}\,\frac{s^2 f(s)}{(xy)^{3/2}}\,ds \qquad (2.44)$$

and observing that

$$G(p)=p\,\frac{d^2}{dp^2}\left[\frac{F(p)}{p}\right]\doteq t^2 f(t),$$

and

$$F(\sqrt{p}) \doteqdot \frac{1}{\sqrt{\pi t}} \int_0^\infty e^{-\frac{s^2}{4t}} f(s)\, ds,$$

where $F(p) \doteqdot f(t)$, we have

$$G(\sqrt{p}) \doteqdot \frac{1}{\sqrt{\pi t}} \int_0^\infty e^{-\frac{s^2}{4t}} s^2 f(s)\, ds.$$

Making the substitution $\frac{1}{t} = \frac{1}{x} + \frac{1}{y}$ in the last relation, and using (2.44) we deduce that

$$pq \frac{F(\sqrt{p}+\sqrt{q})}{\sqrt{p}+\sqrt{q}} \doteqdot \frac{1}{4xy\sqrt{\pi(x+y)}} \Phi\left(\frac{xy}{x+y}\right).$$

10. The Images of the Kelvin Functions

Knowing the images of the Bessel functions it is easy to derive the images of the Kelvin functions and several of their interesting properties. An immediate consequence of the relation

$$J_0(2i\sqrt{xy}) \doteqdot \frac{pq}{pq-1} \tag{2.45}$$

is the relation

$$J_0(2i\sqrt{ixy}) \doteqdot \frac{pq}{pq-i} = \frac{pq(pq+i)}{p^2q^2+1}.$$

By definition

$$J_0(2i\sqrt{ixy}) = \operatorname{ber}(2\sqrt{xy}) + i \operatorname{bei}(2\sqrt{xy}),$$

so that

$$\operatorname{ber}(2\sqrt{xy}) \doteqdot \frac{p^2q^2}{p^2q^2+1}, \tag{2.46}$$

$$\operatorname{bei}(2\sqrt{xy}) = \frac{pq}{p^2q^2+1}. \tag{2.47}$$

Since $\operatorname{bei}(0) = 0$ and $\operatorname{ber}(0) = 1$, we derive easily from (2.46) and (2.47) that

$$\frac{\partial^2}{\partial x\, \partial y} \operatorname{bei}(2\sqrt{xy}) \doteqdot \frac{p^2q^2}{p^2q^2+1} \doteqdot \operatorname{ber}(2\sqrt{xy}) \tag{2.48}$$

and

$$\frac{\partial^2}{\partial x\, \partial y} \operatorname{ber}(2\sqrt{xy}) = -\operatorname{bei}(2\sqrt{xy}). \tag{2.49}$$

On the other hand

$$\operatorname{bei}(2\sqrt{xy}) \doteqdot \frac{1}{pq}\,\frac{p^2q^2}{(pq-i)(pq+i)}\,.$$

and since

$$\frac{pq}{pq-i} \doteqdot J_0\left(2i\sqrt{ixy}\right),$$
$$\frac{pq}{pq+i} \doteqdot J_0\left(2i\sqrt{-ixy}\right),$$

We may apply the multiplication rule to derive the following integral representation of the Kelvin function:

$$\operatorname{bei}\left(2\sqrt{xy}\right) = \int_0^x \int_0^y J_0\left[2i\sqrt{i(x-\xi)(y-\eta)}\right] J_0\left(2i\sqrt{-i\xi\eta}\right) d\xi\, d\eta.$$

11. The Image of a Function of the Product and Quotient of the Arguments

Suppose $F(p) \doteqdot f(x)$. If we consider the transformation with respect to x alone, we can write

$$\frac{p}{p+\frac{1}{q}}\,F\left(p+\frac{1}{q}\right) \doteqdot e^{-\frac{x}{q}} f(x).$$

Now, q occurs only in the first factor of the right side, and the original of $e^{-\frac{x}{q}}$ with respect to q is given by the relation

$$e^{-\frac{x}{q}} \doteqdot J_0\left(2\sqrt{xy}\right).$$

Consequently,

$$\frac{p}{p+\frac{1}{q}}\,F\left(p+\frac{1}{q}\right) \doteqdot J_0\left(2\sqrt{xy}\right) f(x).$$

Replacing p by $\frac{1}{p}$ we transform this relation with the help of

$$pF\left(\frac{1}{p}\right) \doteqdot \int_0^\infty J_0\left(2\sqrt{xs}\right) f(s)\, ds;$$

to obtain

$$\frac{pq}{p+q}\,F\left(\frac{1}{p}+\frac{1}{q}\right) \doteqdot \int_0^\infty J_0\left(2\sqrt{sx}\right) J_0\left(2\sqrt{sy}\right) f(s)\, ds. \quad (2.50)$$

In particular, if $f(x)=e^{-x}$, we have $F(p)=\frac{p}{p+1}$,and evaluating the integral on the right side of (2.50), we obtain

$$\left(1+\frac{1}{p}+\frac{1}{q}\right)^{-1} \doteqdot e^{x+y} J_0\left(2i\sqrt{xy}\right)=e^{x+y} I_0\left(2\sqrt{xy}\right).$$

Again let us suppose that $F(p)\doteq f(x)$. Keeping q constant we have

$$\frac{p}{p+\sqrt{q}} F\left(p+\sqrt{q}\right) \doteq e^{-x\sqrt{q}} f(x)$$

and because

$$\sqrt{q}\cdot e^{-x\sqrt{q}} \doteqdot \frac{e^{-\frac{x^2}{4y}}}{\sqrt{\pi y}},$$

we deduce that

$$\frac{p\sqrt{q}}{p+\sqrt{q}} F\left(p+\sqrt{q}\right) \doteqdot \frac{e^{-\frac{x^2}{4y}}}{\sqrt{\pi y}} f(x).$$

Recalling now that

$$F\left(\sqrt{p}\right) \doteq \frac{1}{\sqrt{\pi x}} \int_0^\infty e^{-\frac{s^2}{4x}} f(s)\, ds,$$

it is easy to derive the relation

$$\frac{\sqrt{pq}}{\sqrt{p}+\sqrt{q}} F\left(\sqrt{p}+\sqrt{q}\right) \doteqdot \frac{1}{\pi\sqrt{xy}} \int_0^\infty e^{-\frac{s^2}{4}\left(\frac{1}{x}+\frac{1}{y}\right)} f(s)\, ds.$$

We shall exhibit several analogous operational relationships.

(1) Let $f(x)\doteq F(p)$ and $F\left(\frac{1}{x}\right)\doteq G(p)$. Then we will have

$$F(p,\ q)=pq\int_0^\infty\int_0^\infty e^{-px-qy} f(xy)\, dx\, dy=$$

$$=q\int_0^\infty e^{-qy}\, dy\cdot p\int_0^\infty e^{-\frac{p}{y}u} f(u)\frac{du}{y}=$$

$$=q\int_0^\infty e^{-qy}F\left(\frac{p}{y}\right)dy=pq\int_0^\infty e^{-pqx}F\left(\frac{1}{x}\right)dx=G(pq).$$

Consequently, $G(pq)\doteqdot f(xy)$. For example

$$\frac{p}{\sqrt{p^2+1}}\doteq J_0(x),$$

and

$$\frac{\pi}{2}p\left[H_0(p)-Y_0(p)\right]\doteq\frac{1}{\sqrt{x^2+1}},$$

whence

$$J_0(xy)\doteqdot\frac{\pi}{2}pq\left[H_0(pq)-Y_0(pq)\right].$$

And in exactly the same way

$$\frac{(xy)^{\frac{n}{2}}}{\Gamma(n+1)}J_n\left(2\sqrt{xy}\right)\doteqdot\frac{pq}{(pq+1)^{n+1}},$$

and

$$J_0\left(2\sqrt{xy}\right)I_1\left(2\sqrt{xy}\right)\doteqdot\frac{pq\left(\sqrt{p^2q^2+1}-pq\right)}{\sqrt{p^2q^2+1}}.$$

(2) Let $f(x)\doteq F(p)$, and $F(x)\doteq G(p)$. Then we will have

$$F(p,q)=pq\int_0^\infty\int_0^\infty e^{-px-qy}f\left(\frac{x}{y}\right)dx\,dy=$$

$$=q\int_0^\infty e^{-qy}dy\cdot p\int_0^\infty e^{-pyu}f(u)\,y\,du=$$

$$=q\int_0^\infty e^{-qy}F(py)\,dy=\frac{q}{p}\int_0^\infty e^{-\frac{q}{p}x}F(x)\,dx=G\left(\frac{q}{p}\right).$$

In this way we can derive the operational relations

$$J_1\left(\frac{x}{y}\right)\doteqdot\frac{\pi}{2}\frac{q}{p}\left[H_1\left(\frac{q}{p}\right)-Y_1\left(\frac{q}{p}\right)-\frac{2}{\pi}\right],$$

and

$$J_0\left(\sqrt{\frac{x}{y}}\right)\doteqdot\sqrt{\frac{q}{p}}K_1\left(\sqrt{\frac{q}{p}}\right).$$

(3) Let $f(x)\doteq F(p)$ and $x^\alpha F\left(\frac{1}{x}\right)\doteq G(p)$. Then

$$F(p,q)=pq\int_0^\infty\int_0^\infty e^{-px-qy}y^\alpha f(xy)\,dx\,dy=$$

$$=q\int_0^\infty e^{-qy}\,dy\,p\int_0^\infty e^{-\frac{p}{y}u}\,y^\alpha f(u)\frac{du}{y}=$$

$$=q\int_0^\infty e^{-qy}\,y^\alpha F\left(\frac{p}{y}\right)dy=pq\int_0^\infty e^{-pqx}\,p^\alpha x^\alpha F\left(\frac{1}{x}\right)dx=p^\alpha G(pq).$$

(4) Let $f(x)\doteqdot F(p)$ and $x^\alpha F(x)\doteqdot G(p)$. Then we find

$$F(p,q)=pq\int_0^\infty\int_0^\infty e^{-px-qy}\,y^\alpha f\left(\frac{x}{y}\right)dx\,dy=$$

$$=q\int_0^\infty e^{-qy}\,dy\cdot p\int_0^\infty e^{-pyu}\,y^\alpha f(u)\,y\,du=$$

$$=q\int_0^\infty e^{-qy}\,y^\alpha F(py)\,dy=\frac{q}{p}\int_0^\infty e^{-\frac{q}{p}x}\frac{1}{p^\alpha}x^\alpha F(x)\,dx=\frac{1}{p^\alpha}G\left(\frac{q}{p}\right).$$

12. The Original of $F\left(\frac{1}{p},\frac{1}{q}\right)$

The relation

$$e^{-\frac{s}{p}-\frac{t}{q}}\doteqdot J_0(2\sqrt{sx})\,J_0(2\sqrt{ty}) \qquad (2.51)$$

holds for $s>0$, $t>0$. If we multiply (2.51) by the function $f(s,t)$ and integrate with respect to s and t over the positive quarter plane, we obtain

$$\int_0^\infty\int_0^\infty e^{-\frac{s}{p}-\frac{t}{q}}f(s,t)\,ds\,dt\doteqdot\int_0^\infty\int_0^\infty J_0(2\sqrt{sx})J_0(2\sqrt{ty})f(s,t)\,ds\,dt.$$

i.e. if $F(p,q)\doteqdot f(x,y)$ this may be written

$$pq\,F\left(\frac{1}{p},\frac{1}{q}\right)\doteqdot\int_0^\infty\int_0^\infty J_0(2\sqrt{sx})\,J_0(2\sqrt{ty})\,f(s,t)\,ds\,dt. \qquad (2.52)$$

For example, since

$$F(p,q)=\frac{pq}{p^2q^2+1}\doteqdot \operatorname{bei}(2\sqrt{xy}),$$

then

$$pq\,F\left(\frac{1}{p},\frac{1}{q}\right)=\frac{p^2q^2}{p^2q^2+1}\doteqdot \operatorname{ber}(2\sqrt{xy})$$

and consequently

$$\operatorname{ber}(2\sqrt{xy})=\int_0^\infty\int_0^\infty J_0(2\sqrt{sx})J_0(2\sqrt{ty})\operatorname{bei}(2\sqrt{st})\,ds\,dt. \tag{2.53}$$

In the same way, when

$$F(p,\ q)=\frac{pq(p+q)}{(p^2+1)(q^2+1)}\doteqdot\sin(x+y),$$

we obtain

$$pqF\left(\frac{1}{p},\ \frac{1}{q}\right)=\frac{pq(p+q)}{(p^2+1)(q^2+1)}\doteqdot\sin(x+y)$$

and therefore

$$\sin(x+y)=\int_0^\infty\int_0^\infty J_0(2\sqrt{sx})J_0(2\sqrt{ty})\sin(s+t)\,ds\,dt.$$

13. The Original of $F(\sqrt{p},\ \sqrt{q})$

We start from two known operational relations:

$$\sqrt{p}\,e^{-s\sqrt{p}}\doteqdot\frac{e^{-\frac{s^2}{4x}}}{\sqrt{\pi x}}, \tag{2.54}$$

$$\sqrt{q}\,e^{-t\sqrt{q}}\doteqdot\frac{e^{-\frac{t^2}{4y}}}{\sqrt{\pi y}}. \tag{2.55}$$

We first multiply together the symbolic equations (2.54) and (2.55). If we now multiply both sides by $f(s,\ t)$ and integrate with respect to s and t over the positive quarter plane, we obtain

$$F(\sqrt{p},\sqrt{q})\doteqdot\frac{1}{\pi\sqrt{xy}}\int_0^\infty\int_0^\infty e^{-\frac{s^2}{4x}-\frac{t^2}{4y}}f(s,\ t)\,ds\,dt. \tag{2.56}$$

For example, let

$$f(x,\ y)=\operatorname{ber}(2\sqrt{xy})\doteqdot\frac{p^2q^2}{p^2q^2+1}.$$

Then

$$F(\sqrt{p}, \sqrt{q}) = \frac{pq}{pq+1} \doteqdot J_0(2\sqrt{xy})$$

and consequently

$$J_0(2\sqrt{xy}) = \frac{1}{\pi\sqrt{xy}} \int_0^\infty \int_0^\infty e^{-\frac{s^2}{4x}-\frac{t^2}{4y}} \operatorname{ber}(2\sqrt{st})\, ds\, dt. \quad (2.57)$$

If in equation (2.56) we write $s^2 = u$, $t^2 = v$, we derive

$$F(\sqrt{p}, \sqrt{q}) \doteqdot \frac{1}{4\pi\sqrt{xy}} \int_0^\infty \int_0^\infty e^{-\frac{u}{4x}-\frac{v}{4y}} \frac{f(\sqrt{u}, \sqrt{v})}{\sqrt{uv}}\, du\, dv. \quad (2.58)$$

If we suppose that $F(p, q) \doteqdot f(x, y)$ and $G(p, q) \doteqdot \frac{f(\sqrt{x}, \sqrt{y})}{\sqrt{xy}}$, this becomes

$$F(\sqrt{p}, \sqrt{q}) \doteqdot \frac{4\sqrt{xy}}{\pi} G\left(\frac{1}{4x}, \frac{1}{4y}\right).$$

Thus we have the system of operational relations

$$\left.\begin{aligned} &F(p, q) \doteqdot f(x, y), \\ &G(p, q) \doteqdot \frac{f(\sqrt{x}, \sqrt{y})}{\sqrt{xy}} \\ &F(\sqrt{p}, \sqrt{q}) \doteqdot \frac{4\sqrt{xy}}{\pi} G\left(\frac{1}{4x}, \frac{1}{4y}\right) \end{aligned}\right\} \quad (2.59)$$

with the help of which it is always possible to calculate one of the six functions, when the others are known. For example, using (2.59), we can derive the following:

(1) The image of the function $\frac{f(\sqrt{x}, \sqrt{y})}{\sqrt{xy}}$ from the original of the function $F(\sqrt{p}, \sqrt{q})$ by replacing x and y by $\frac{1}{4p}$ and $\frac{1}{4q}$ respectively, and finally multiplying by $\pi\sqrt{pq}$.

(2) The original of the function $F(\sqrt{p}, \sqrt{q})$ from the image of the function $\frac{f(\sqrt{x}, \sqrt{y})}{\sqrt{xy}}$ by replacing p and q by $\frac{1}{4x}$ and $\frac{1}{4y}$ respectively, and finally multiplying by $\frac{4}{\pi}\sqrt{xy}$.

(3) The image of the function $xyf(x^2, y^2)$ from the image of the function $\sqrt{xy}\; f\left(\frac{1}{x}, \frac{1}{y}\right)$ by replacing p and q by $\frac{p^2}{4}$ and $\frac{q^2}{4}$ respectively, and finally multiplying by π.

(4) The original of the function $F(p^2, q^2)$ from the original of the function $\pi\sqrt{pq}\,F\left(\frac{1}{4p}, \frac{1}{4q}\right)$ by replacing x and y by x^2 and y^2 respectively, and finally multiplying by xy.

(5) The image of the function $\sqrt{xy}\,f\left(\frac{1}{x}, \frac{1}{y}\right)$ from the image of the function $xyf(x^2, y^2)$ and replacing p and q by $2\sqrt{p}$ and $2\sqrt{q}$, respectively, and finally multiplying by π.

(6) The original of the function $\sqrt{pq}\,F\left(\frac{1}{4p}, \frac{1}{4q}\right)$ from the original of the function $F(p^2, q^2)$ by replacing x and y by $\sqrt{x}$ and $\sqrt{y}$ respectively, and finally multiplying by $\frac{1}{\pi\sqrt{xy}}$.

We can obtain the following system of operational relations in a similar way:

$$\left.\begin{aligned} &F(p, q) \doteqdot f(x, y), \\ &G(p, q) \doteqdot f(\sqrt{x}, \sqrt{y}), \\ &\sqrt{pq}\,F(\sqrt{p}, \sqrt{q}) \doteqdot \frac{1}{\pi\sqrt{xy}}\,G\left(\frac{1}{4x}, \frac{1}{4y}\right) \end{aligned}\right\}, \quad (2.60)$$

and in the same way

$$\left.\begin{aligned} &F(p, q) \doteqdot f(x, y), \\ &G(p, q) \doteqdot \frac{1}{\sqrt{x}}\,f(\sqrt{x}, \sqrt{y}), \\ &\sqrt{q}\,F(\sqrt{p}, \sqrt{q}) \doteqdot \frac{2}{\pi}\sqrt{\frac{x}{y}}\,G\left(\frac{1}{4x}, \frac{1}{4y}\right), \end{aligned}\right\} \quad (2.61)$$

and

$$\left.\begin{aligned} &F(p, q) \doteqdot f(x, y), \\ &G(p, q) \doteqdot \frac{1}{\sqrt{y}}\,f(\sqrt{x}, \sqrt{y}), \\ &\sqrt{p}\,F(\sqrt{p}, \sqrt{q}) \doteqdot \frac{2}{\pi}\sqrt{\frac{y}{x}}\,G\left(\frac{1}{4x}, \frac{1}{4y}\right) \end{aligned}\right\} \quad (2.62)$$

For each of the systems (2.60), (2.61), and (2.62) we can formulate six rules analogous to those just mentioned for the system (2.59).

For example, using (2.60) we can derive

(1) The original of the function $\frac{1}{p}F(p^2, q^2)$ from the original of the function $\frac{\pi}{2\sqrt{pq}}F\left(\frac{1}{4p}, \frac{1}{4q}\right)$ by replacing x and y by x^2 and y^2 respectively.

(2) The image of the function $f(x^2, y^2)$ from the image of the function $\frac{1}{\sqrt{xy}}f\left(\frac{1}{4x}, \frac{1}{4y}\right)$ by replacing p and q by p^2 and q^2 respectively, and finally multiplying by πpq.

14. The Image of the Function $f(\sqrt{x^2+y^2})$

Let

$$f(x) \doteqdot F(p) = p\Phi(p),$$

so that

$$xf(x) \doteqdot -p\Phi'(p).$$

We shall use this observation to evaluate the integral

$$F(p, q) = pq\int_0^\infty\int_0^\infty e^{-px-qy}f\left(\sqrt{x^2+y^2}\right)dx\,dy.$$

Transforming to polar co-ordinates

$$x = \rho\cos\varphi, \quad y = \rho\sin\varphi,$$

we have

$$F(p, q) = pq\int_0^{\frac{\pi}{2}}d\theta\int_0^\infty e^{-(p\cos\theta+q\sin\theta)\rho}\rho f(\rho)\,d\rho =$$

$$= -pq\int_0^{\frac{\pi}{2}}\Phi'(p\cos\theta + q\sin\theta)\,d\theta.$$

If we write

$$u = p\cos\theta + q\sin\theta, \quad R^2 = p^2 + q^2.$$

then

$$du = (-p\sin\theta + q\cos\theta)\,d\theta = \pm\sqrt{R^2 - u^2}\,d\theta$$

and

$$F(p,q)=pq\int_0^\infty\int_0^\infty e^{-px-qy}f\left(\sqrt{x^2+y^2}\right)dx\,dy=$$
$$=-pq\int_p^R \Phi'(u)\frac{du}{\sqrt{R^2-u^2}}-pq\int_q^R \Phi'(u)\frac{du}{\sqrt{R^2-u^2}}. \tag{2.63}$$

15. Laguerre Polynomials

In this section we shall consider the Laguerre polynomials

$$L_n(x)=\frac{e^x}{n!}\frac{d^n}{dx^n}(x^n e^{-x}), \tag{2.64}$$

which occur often in applications.

We start from the operational relation

$$\left(1-\frac{1}{p}\right)^n=F(p)\doteqdot L_n(x) \tag{2.65}$$

and applying the shift rule for images,

$$\frac{p}{p+\lambda}F(p+\lambda)\doteqdot e^{-\lambda x}f(x), \tag{2.66}$$

to (2.65) with $\lambda=1$ we obtain

$$\frac{p}{p+1}\left(1-\frac{1}{p+1}\right)^n=\left(\frac{p}{p+1}\right)^{n+1}\doteqdot e^{-x}L_n(x). \tag{2.67}$$

Replacing x by y and p by q we have

$$\left(\frac{q}{q+1}\right)^{n+1}\doteqdot e^{-y}L_n(y). \tag{2.68}$$

From the well known operational relations

$$\ln(1+p)\doteqdot\int_x^\infty\frac{e^{-t}}{t}dt \tag{2.69}$$

and

$$\ln(1+q)\doteqdot\int_y^\infty\frac{e^{-t}}{t}dt,$$

we can find an explicit expression for the bilinear form

$$e^{-x-y}\sum_{n=0}^\infty\frac{L_n(x)L_n(y)}{n+1}=K(x,y). \tag{2.70}$$

We shall prove that

$$K(x, y) = \begin{cases} \int\limits_y^\infty \frac{e^{-t}\,dt}{t} & \text{for} \quad x < y, \\ \int\limits_x^\infty \frac{e^{-t}\,dt}{t} & \text{for} \quad x > y. \end{cases} \tag{2.71}$$

In fact, from (2.67) and (2.68) we have

$$e^{-x-y}\, L_n(x)\, L_n(y) \doteqdot \left(\frac{pq}{(1+p)(1+q)}\right)^{n+1}.$$

Consequently

$$\sum_{n=0}^{\infty} \frac{L_n(x)\, L_n(y)}{n+1} = K(x, y) \doteqdot -\ln\left(1 - \frac{pq}{(1+p)(1+q)}\right)$$

or

$$K(x, y) \doteqdot \ln(1+p) + \ln(1+q) - \ln(1+p+q). \tag{2.72}$$

On the other hand, if we write

$$f(x) = \int\limits_x^\infty \frac{e^{-t}}{t}\, dt,$$

then, according to (2.69), $F(p) = \ln(1+p)$, and equation (2.16) becomes

$$f(M) \doteqdot \ln(1+p) + \ln(1+q) - \ln(1+p+q); \tag{2.73}$$

from (2.72) and (2.73) we obtain (2.71). By the application of (2.15) we obtain the further relation

$$\ln(1+p+q) \doteqdot \begin{cases} \int\limits_x^\infty \frac{e^{-t}}{t}\, dt & \text{for} \quad x < y, \\ \int\limits_y^\infty \frac{e^{-t}}{t}\, dt & \text{for} \quad x > y. \end{cases} \tag{2.74}$$

We shall prove one more relation involving the Laguerre polynomials, namely,

$$\left.\begin{aligned} \sum_{n=0}^{\infty} L_n(x)\, L_n(y)\, \lambda^n = \frac{1}{1-\lambda} \cdot e^{-\frac{\lambda(x+y)}{1-\lambda}}\, I_0\left(\frac{2\sqrt{\lambda x y}}{1-\lambda}\right), \\ |\lambda| < 1. \end{aligned}\right\} \tag{2.75}$$

From (2.65) we have

$$\left(1-\frac{1}{q}\right)^n \doteqdot L_n(y). \tag{2.76}$$

Therefore,

$$\sum_{n=0}^{\infty} L_n(x) L_n(y) \lambda^n \mathrel{\ddot{=}} \sum_{n=0}^{\infty} \left[\left(1-\frac{1}{p}\right)\left(1-\frac{1}{q}\right)\lambda\right]^n$$

or

$$\sum_{n=0}^{\infty} L_n(x) L_n(y)\, \lambda^n \mathrel{\ddot{=}} \frac{1}{1-\lambda}\, \frac{pq}{pq+\dfrac{\lambda}{1-\lambda}(p+q)-\dfrac{\lambda}{1-\lambda}}. \tag{2.77}$$

We obtain the original of the right side by means of the relation

$$\frac{pq}{pq-ap-bq+c} \mathrel{\ddot{=}} e^{bx+ay} J_0\left(2\sqrt{(c-ab)\,xy}\right). \tag{2.78}$$

Then (2.75) follows from (2.77) and (2.78).

16. The Evaluation of Integrals

In this section we shall consider the application of our operational calculus to the evaluation of integrals. In the first place, the integrals which we shall consider can be thought of either as originals or as images. It may also be possible to introduce an arbitrary parameter under the integral sign leading to a simplification of the calculation, from which we may obtain the value of the desired integral by assigning a particular value to the parameter in the end. Finally, we can make use of the formulae of the operational calculus in one variable which arise from the corresponding relations in two variables when we replace one of the arguments by a function of the other. For example, according to equation (2.30) we have

$$\frac{F(p,p)}{p} \doteqdot \int_0^x f(x-s,s)\,ds.$$

Consequently, if the image $F(p, q)$ is known for the function $f(x, y)$ and if the original of the function $\frac{F(p,p)}{p}$ is known then we can evaluate the integral

$$F(x) = \int_0^x f(x-s,s)\,ds.$$

In a similar way it is possible to make use of other operational relations, such as

$$\frac{1}{p} F(\sqrt{p}, p) \doteqdot \int_0^\infty ds \int_0^x \frac{1}{\sqrt{\pi(x-t)}} e^{-\frac{s^2}{4(x-t)}} f(s, t)\, dt, \quad (2.79)$$

$$\frac{F(\sqrt{p}, \sqrt{p})}{\sqrt{p}} \doteqdot \int_0^\infty ds \int_0^x \frac{s}{2\sqrt{\pi (x-t)^3}} e^{-\frac{s^2}{4(x-t)}} f(s, t)\, dt. \quad (2.80)$$

We give some examples of the evaluation of integrals.

(1)

$$F(x) = \int_0^\infty \sin xs \cos s \frac{ds}{s}.$$

We introduce an auxiliary parameter y defining the function

$$F(x, y) = \int_0^\infty \sin xs \cos ys \frac{ds}{s}.$$

Since

$$\sin xs \doteqdot \frac{ps}{p^2+s^2}, \qquad \cos ys \doteqdot \frac{q^2}{q^2+s^2},$$

we derive

$$F(x, y) \doteqdot \int_0^\infty \frac{ps}{p^2+s^2} \frac{q^2}{q^2+s^2} \frac{ds}{s} = \frac{\pi}{2} \frac{q}{p+q}.$$

We translate the right side of this last relation back to its original,

$$\frac{\pi}{2} \frac{q}{p+q} \doteqdot \begin{cases} 0 & \text{for } x < y, \\ \frac{\pi}{2} & \text{for } x > y. \end{cases}$$

Setting $y = 1$, we obtain finally

$$F(x) = \begin{cases} \frac{\pi}{2} & \text{for } x > 1, \\ 0 & \text{for } x < 1. \end{cases}$$

(2)

$$F(x) = \int_0^\infty \sin xs \sin \frac{1}{s} \frac{ds}{s}.$$

As before we introduce an auxiliary parameter y by defining the function

$$F(x, y) = \int_0^\infty \sin xs \sin \frac{y}{s} \frac{ds}{s}.$$

We know that

$$\sin xs \doteqdot \frac{ps}{p^2+s^2}, \qquad \sin\frac{y}{s} \doteqdot \frac{qs}{q^2s^2+1},$$

from which we can write down

$$F(x, y) \doteqdot\doteqdot \int_0^\infty \frac{pq}{(p^2+s^2)(q^2s^2+1)}\,ds = \frac{\pi}{2}\,\frac{q}{pq+1}.$$

Making use of the relation

$$\frac{q}{pq+a} \doteqdot\doteqdot \sqrt{\frac{x}{ay}}\,J_1(2\sqrt{axy}), \quad (a \neq 0),$$

we derive

$$F(x, y) = \frac{\pi}{2}\sqrt{\frac{x}{y}}\,J_1(2\sqrt{xy}).$$

Finally, setting $y=1$ we obtain

$$F(x) = \frac{\pi}{2}\sqrt{x}J_1(2\sqrt{x}).$$

(3) $$F(x) = \int_0^a \operatorname{ber}[2\sqrt{s(x-s)}]\,ds.$$

Let

$$F(p, q) = \frac{p^2q^2}{p^2q^2+1} \doteqdot\doteqdot \operatorname{ber}(2\sqrt{xy}). \tag{2.81}$$

Then

$$\frac{F(p, p)}{p} = \frac{p^3}{p^4+1} \doteqdot \frac{1}{\sqrt{2}}\left(\cos\frac{x}{\sqrt{2}}\operatorname{sh}\frac{x}{\sqrt{2}} + \sin\frac{x}{\sqrt{2}}\operatorname{ch}\frac{x}{\sqrt{2}}\right). \tag{2.82}$$

According to (2.30) we have therefore

$$F(x) = \int_0^x \operatorname{ber}[2\sqrt{(x-s)s}]\,ds =$$

$$= \frac{1}{\sqrt{2}}\left[\cos\frac{x}{\sqrt{2}}\operatorname{sh}\frac{x}{\sqrt{2}} + \sin\frac{x}{\sqrt{2}}\operatorname{ch}\frac{x}{\sqrt{2}}\right]. \tag{2.83}$$

(4) $$F(x) = \int_0^\infty ds \int_0^x \frac{1}{\pi\sqrt{x-t}}\,e^{-\frac{s^2}{4(x-t)}}\operatorname{ber}(2\sqrt{st})\,dt.$$

Applying (2.79) and (2.81) we find

$$F(x) \doteqdot \frac{p^2}{p^3+1} \doteqdot -\frac{1}{3}\left(e^{-x}+\varepsilon^2 e^{-\varepsilon x}+\varepsilon e^{-\varepsilon^2 x}\right),$$

where $\varepsilon \neq 1$ and $\varepsilon^3 = 1$.

(5) $J = \int\limits_0^{\frac{\pi}{2}} e^{-\operatorname{tg}^2\varphi}\, d\varphi.$

If we change the variable of integration by the relations

$$x - s = x\cos^2\varphi, \qquad s = x\sin^2\varphi, \tag{2.84}$$

we obtain

$$J = \frac{1}{2}\int\limits_0^{x} \frac{e^{-\frac{s}{x-s}}}{\sqrt{s(x-s)}}\, ds.$$

Since

$$F(p, q) = \pi\sqrt{pq}\, e^{-\frac{p}{q}} \operatorname{erfc}\left(\sqrt{-\frac{p}{q}}\right) \doteqdot \frac{\sqrt{\pi q}}{\sqrt{x-\frac{1}{q}}} \doteqdot \frac{e^{-\frac{y}{x}}}{\sqrt{xy}},$$

(p.155, no. 8.7) we find

$$\frac{F(p,p)}{p} = \frac{\pi}{e}\operatorname{erfc}(i).$$

Finally, making use of (2.30), we derive the value of the integral

$$\int\limits_0^{\frac{\pi}{2}} e^{-\operatorname{tg}^2\varphi}\, d\varphi = \frac{\pi}{2e}\operatorname{erfc}(i).$$

(6) $J = \int\limits_0^{\frac{\pi}{2}} e^{-\operatorname{tg}^2\varphi} \operatorname{tg}\varphi\, d\varphi.$

Applying the transformation (2.84) this becomes

$$J = \frac{1}{2}\int\limits_0^{x} \frac{e^{-\frac{s}{x-s}}}{x-s}\, ds.$$

We have

$$F(p, q) = -pe^{\frac{p}{q}} \operatorname{Ei}\left(-\frac{p}{q}\right) \doteqdot \frac{1}{x+\frac{1}{q}} \doteqdot \frac{1}{x}\, e^{-\frac{y}{x}}$$

(p.153, no. 7.7) and consequently

$$\frac{F(p,p)}{p} = -e\,\mathrm{Ei}(-1).$$

According to (2.30) we obtain therefore

$$\int_0^{\frac{\pi}{2}} e^{-\mathrm{tg}^2 \varphi} \,\mathrm{tg}\,\varphi \, d\varphi = -\frac{e}{2}\,\mathrm{Ei}\,(-1).$$

17. Differential Equations

One of the most important reasons for the widespread use of the operational calculus lies in its application to the solution of differential equations. Laplace himself showed that his transform reduces linear ordinary differential equations with constant coefficients to algebraic equations. However, it is only recently that the two-dimensional Laplace transform has been applied to the solution of partial differential equations. The two-dimensional procedure is similar to that of the one-dimensional case. We pass through three stages:

(1) Obtaining the transformed equation.

(2) Finding the solution of the transformed equation.

(3) Translating the solution of the transformed equation into the desired solution.

In carrying out this procedure we encounter difficulties peculiar to the operational calculus in two dimensions. Since the equations we are considering are partial differential equations it will be necessary to specify boundary conditions, and in the first stage it is sometimes necessary to demand more initial or boundary conditions than the problem requires. Having introduced these extra conditions at the first stage, however, we find that we can eliminate them at the second stage by examining the analytic properties of the solution of the transformed equation. Finally, at the third stage, we pass from the solution of the transformed equation to the solution of the original equation by means of tables or with the help of the inversion formula.

We remark that the variables x and y are supposed to be real and positive.

1. Equations of the first order.

We begin by studying the first order linear equation

$$\frac{\partial u}{\partial x} + \frac{\partial u}{\partial y} = f(x, y), \quad 0 < x < \infty, \quad 0 < y < \infty. \quad (2.85)$$

In order to apply the operational calculus and find the images of $\frac{\partial u}{\partial x}$ and $\frac{\partial u}{\partial y}$, we must know the values of the function $u(x,y)$ at $x=0$ and $y=0$, i.e., $u(0, y)=a(y)$ and $u(x, 0)=b(x)$. Let

$$\left.\begin{aligned} u(x, y) &\doteqdot U(p, q), \\ f(x, y) &\doteqdot F(p, q), \\ a(y) &\doteq A(q), \\ b(x) &\doteq B(p) \end{aligned}\right\}. \tag{2.86}$$

With this notation we obtain the transformed equation

$$p\{U(p, q)-A(q)\}+q\{U(p, q)-B(p)\}=F(p, q),$$

from which we can easily write down the solution

$$U(p, q)=\frac{F(p, q)}{p+q}+\frac{p}{p+q}A(q)+\frac{q}{p+q}B(p).$$

From (2.16) and (2.18) we have

$$\frac{p}{p+q}A(q)\doteqdot\begin{cases} 0 & \text{for } x>y, \\ a(y-x) & \text{for } x<y; \end{cases}$$

$$\frac{q}{p+q}B(p)\doteqdot\begin{cases} 0 & \text{for } x<y, \\ b(x-y) & \text{for } x>y. \end{cases}$$

Finally, applying (2.22), we obtain the desired solution

$$u(x, y)=\begin{cases} b(x-y)+\int\limits_0^y f(x-s, y-s)\,ds & \text{for } x>y, \\ a(y-x)+\int\limits_0^x f(x-s, y-s)\,ds & \text{for } x<y. \end{cases}$$

From this it follows that if $a(0)=b(0)$ the function $u(x, y)$ is defined and continuous in the region $R(0\leqslant x<\infty, 0\leqslant y<\infty)$ and differentiable for $y>x$ and $y<x$. The functions $a(y)$ and $b(x)$ do not depend on each other and the method of deriving the solution supposes that these functions possess Laplace transforms.

We remark that the existence and uniqueness of an analytic solution of the equation (2.85) is determined by the values on the axis $x=0$, i.e. by $a(y)$ alone. The fact that we are given an independent function $b(x)$ does not contradict this statement since the general solution is not usually analytic along the line $y=x$.

We consider next the equation

$$\frac{\partial u}{\partial x}-\frac{\partial u}{\partial y}=f(x, y),\ 0<x<\infty,\ 0<y<\infty. \qquad (2.87)$$

In the notation of (2.86) the transformed equation takes the form

$$p\{U(p, q)-A(q)\}-q\{U(p, q)-B(p)\}=F(p, q).$$

so that

$$U(p, q)=\frac{F(p, q)+pA(q)-qB(p)}{p-q}. \qquad (2.88)$$

Because the image of the required solution must be an analytic function for all values of p and q in the region defined by the inequalities $\operatorname{Re} p>\alpha$, $\operatorname{Re} q>\beta$ (where α and β are two suitably chosen constants), the numerator of the right side of (2.88) must be equal to zero when $p=q$, in other words

$$pA(p)-pB(p)+F(p, p)=0. \qquad (2.89)$$

Going back to the originals we obtain a relation between the functions $a(x)$ and $b(y)$

$$a(x)-b(x)+\int_0^x f(x-s, s)\,ds=0. \qquad (2.90)$$

Thus it turns out, in this case, that the functions $a(y)$ and $b(x)$ cannot be chosen independently of each other, and the operational calculus enables us to eliminate a superfluous initial condition. We call the relation (2.90) "the condition of consistency" of the initial conditions. If it is satisfied then the function $U(p, q)$ in (2.88) is the image of the required solution of (2.87).

Substituting in (2.88) the value of $B(p)$ from (2.89) we obtain

$$U(p, q)=\frac{pA(q)-qA(p)}{p-q}+\frac{F(p,q)}{p-q}-\frac{q}{p}\,\frac{F(p, p)}{p-q}. \qquad (2.91)$$

According to (2.31) the original of the first fraction on the right side of this equation is the function $a(x+y)$. Writing the second fraction in the form $\frac{1}{q}F(p, q)\frac{q}{p-q}$, it is easy to find the original with respect to q. In fact, since

$$\frac{q}{q-p} \doteqdot e^{py}, \quad F(p, q) \doteqdot F_1(p, y),$$

we apply the convolution theorem to obtain

$$\frac{1}{q} F(p, q) \frac{q}{q-p} \doteqdot e^{+py} \int_0^y e^{-ps} F_1(p, s)\, ds. \tag{2.92}$$

Further, since

$$\frac{F(p, p)}{p} = \int_0^\infty e^{-py} F_1(p, y)\, dy,$$

we have

$$\frac{q}{q-p} \frac{F(p, p)}{p} \doteqdot e^{py} \int_0^\infty e^{-ps} F_1(p, s)\, ds. \tag{2.93}$$

From (2.92) and (2.93) it follows that

$$\frac{F(p, q)}{p-q} - \frac{q}{p} \frac{F(p, p)}{p-q} \doteqdot \int_y^\infty e^{-p(s-y)} F_1(p, s)\, ds. \tag{2.94}$$

By the shift rule for original functions we have

$$e^{-p(s-y)} F_1(p, s) \doteqdot \begin{cases} 0 & \text{for } x < s-y, \\ f(x+y-s, s) & \\ \quad \text{for } x > s-y. \end{cases} \tag{2.95}$$

Finally, combining (2.94) and (2.95), we derive

$$\frac{F(p, q)}{p-q} - \frac{q}{p} \frac{F(p, p)}{p-q} \doteqdot \int_y^{x+y} f(x+y-s, s)\, ds =$$

$$= \int_0^x f(x-s, y+s)\, ds. \tag{2.96}$$

Consequently, the solution of (2.87) takes the form

$$u(x, y) = a(x+y) + \int_0^x f(x-s, y+s)\, ds.$$

We remark that this solution could equally well have been expressed in terms of the function $b(x)$.

2. Second order equations of hyperbolic type.

We consider the equation for the vibrating string,

$$\frac{\partial^2 u}{\partial x^2} - \frac{\partial^2 u}{\partial y^2} = f(x, y), \; 0 < x < \infty, \; 0 < y < \infty. \tag{2.97}$$

To apply the operational method we require the functions

$$\left.\begin{aligned} u(0, y) &= a(y) \doteqdot A(q), \\ \left(\frac{\partial u}{\partial x}\right)_{x=0} &= c(y) \doteqdot C(q), \\ u(x, 0) &= b(x) \doteqdot B(p), \\ \left(\frac{\partial u}{\partial y}\right)_{y=0} &= d(x) \doteqdot D(p). \end{aligned}\right\} \tag{2.98}$$

As usual we use the notations

$$u(x, y) \doteqdot\doteqdot U(p, q), \quad f(x, y) \doteqdot\doteqdot F(p, q). \tag{2.99}$$

All the Laplace transforms in (2.98) and (2.99) are supposed to exist. In order to ensure the continuity of the function $u(x, y)$ at the origin we shall also assume that $a(0) = b(0)$. With these notations the transformed equation takes the form

$$p^2\{U(p, q) - A(q)\} - pC(q) - \\ - q^2\{U(p, q) - B(p)\} + qD(p) = F(p, q),$$

whose formal solution is

$$U(p, q) = \frac{F(p, q) + pC(q) - qD(p) + p^2 A(q) - q^2 B(p)}{p^2 - q^2}. \tag{2.100}$$

Now the function $U(p, q)$ is a Laplace transform so that the numerator on the right side of (2.100) must be zero when $p = q$. Thus we have

$$F(p, p) + pC(p) - pD(p) + p^2\{A(p) - B(p)\} = 0,$$

which we may write in the following form

$$\frac{F(p, p)}{p} + C(p) - D(p) + p\{A(p) - a(0)\} - \\ - p\{B(p) - b(0)\} = 0. \tag{2.101}$$

We can write down the original of this relation

$$\int_0^x f(x - s, s)\, ds + c(x) - d(x) + \frac{\partial}{\partial x}\{a(x) - b(x)\} = 0,$$

from which it follows that one of the four functions a, b, c, d

is determined by the other three.

Although it is necessary to establish the notations (2.98) in order to derive the solution (2.100) of the transformed equation, we can pass to the original without actually evaluating the transforms $A(p)$, $B(p)$, $C(p)$, $D(p)$ and without having recourse to the inversion formula. In fact, eliminating $D(p)$ from the right side of (2.100), we have

$$U(p, q) = \frac{pF(p, q) - qF(p, p)}{p(p^2 - q^2)} + \frac{pC(q) - qC(p)}{p^2 - q^2} + \\ + p\left\{\frac{pA(q) - qA(p)}{p^2 - q^2}\right\} + \frac{qB(p)}{p+q}. \tag{2.102}$$

Using (2.22) and (2.96) we obtain the original of the first term:

$$\frac{pF(p, q) - qF(p, p)}{p(p^2 - q^2)} \doteqdot \int_0^{\min(x, y)} ds \int_0^{x-s} f(x - s - t, y - s + t)\, dt.$$

From (2.22) and (2.31) we obtain

$$\frac{pC(q) - qC(p)}{p^2 - q^2} \doteqdot \int_0^{\min(x, y)} c(x + y - 2s)\, ds.$$

Writing the third fraction in the form

$$p\left[\frac{pA(q) - qA(p)}{p^2 - q^2}\right] = \frac{1}{2}\,\frac{pA(q) - qA(p)}{p - q} + \frac{1}{2}\,\frac{pA(q)}{p+q} - \frac{1}{2}\,\frac{qA(p)}{p+q}$$

and making use of (2.31), (2.38) and (2.39) we find

$$p\left[\frac{pA(q) - qA(p)}{p^2 - q^2}\right] \doteqdot \begin{cases} \frac{1}{2}\{a(x+y) + a(y-x)\} & \text{for } y > x, \\ \frac{1}{2}\{a(x+y) - a(x-y)\} & \text{for } y < x. \end{cases}$$

Finally, we can write down the original of the fourth term

$$\frac{qB(p)}{p+q} \doteq e^{-py} B(p) \doteq \begin{cases} b(x - y) & \text{for } x > y, \\ 0 & \text{for } x < y. \end{cases}$$

Consequently, the required solution is given by

$$u(x, y) = \int_0^{\min(x, y)} ds \int_0^{x-s} f(x - s - t, y - s + t)\, dt +$$

$$+\int_0^{\min(x,y)} c(x+y-2s)\,ds+\frac{1}{2}a(x+y)+$$

$$+\begin{cases}\frac{1}{2}a(y-x) & \text{for } x<y,\\ b(x-y)-\frac{1}{2}a(x-y) & \text{for } x>y.\end{cases}$$

3. Second order equations of parabolic type.

We consider the equation of heat conduction,

$$\frac{\partial^2 u}{\partial x^2}-\frac{\partial u}{\partial y}=f(x, y),\ 0<x<\infty,\ 0<y<\infty. \quad (2.103)$$

Let

$$u(x, y) \doteqdot U(p, q),\ f(x, y) \doteqdot F(p, q)$$

and let us suppose that we are given the initial conditions

$$u(x, 0)=a(x) \doteq A(p),$$
$$u(0, y)=b(y) \doteq B(q),$$
$$\left(\frac{\partial u}{\partial x}\right)_{x=0}=c(y) \doteq C(q).$$

Transforming the equation (2.103) we obtain

$$p^2[U(p, q)-B(q)]-pC(q)-q[U(p, q)-A(p)]=F(p, q),$$

from which we derive

$$U(p, q)=\frac{F(p, q)-qA(p)+pC(q)+p^2B(q)}{p^2-q}. \quad (2.104)$$

The denominator in (2.104) has zeros $p=\sqrt{q}$ and $p=-\sqrt{q}$. The second zero $p=-\sqrt{q}$ does not interest us since it will not lie in the region of convergence of the Laplace integral if $\operatorname{Re} q$ is sufficiently large. On the other hand the first zero $p=\sqrt{q}$ will lie in the region of convergence and therefore our previous argument applies: since $U(p, q)$ must be analytic inside its region of convergence it follows that the numerator of the right side of (2.104) must have a zero at $p=\sqrt{q}$, and we obtain the relation

$$F(\sqrt{q}, q) - qA(\sqrt{q}) + \sqrt{q}\, C(q) + qB(q) = 0, \quad (2.105)$$

connecting the functions $a(x)$, $b(x)$ and $c(x)$, so that only two of them can be chosen arbitrarily. If we suppose, for example, that the functions $a(x)$ and $c(x)$ are known, then we deduce from (2.105) that

$$B(p) = -\frac{F(\sqrt{p}, p)}{p} + A(\sqrt{p}) - \frac{C(p)}{\sqrt{p}}. \quad (2.106)$$

According to (2.79) we have

$$\frac{F(\sqrt{p}, p)}{p} \doteqdot \int_0^\infty ds \int_0^x \frac{1}{\sqrt{\pi(x-t)}} e^{-\frac{s^2}{4(x-t)}} f(s, t)\, dt, \quad (2.107)$$

and the original of $A(\sqrt{p})$ is well known:

$$A(\sqrt{p}) \doteqdot \frac{1}{\sqrt{\pi x}} \int_0^\infty e^{-\frac{s^2}{4x}} a(s)\, ds. \quad (2.108)$$

There remains the third term of (2.106): we need to find the original of the function

$$\frac{C(p)}{\sqrt{p}} = \sqrt{p} \int_0^\infty e^{-ps} c(s)\, ds.$$

This follows simply from the relation

$$e^{-ps}\sqrt{p} \doteqdot \begin{cases} 0 & \text{for } x < s, \\ \dfrac{1}{\sqrt{\pi(x-s)}} & \text{for } x > s, \end{cases}$$

so that

$$\frac{C(p)}{\sqrt{p}} \doteqdot \int_0^x \frac{c(s)}{\sqrt{\pi(x-s)}} ds. \quad (2.109)$$

Substituting (2.107), (2.108) and (2.109) in (2.106) we obtain finally

$$b(x) = -\int_0^\infty ds \int_0^x \frac{1}{\pi\sqrt{x-t}} e^{-\frac{s^2}{4(x-t)}} f(s, t)\, dt +$$

$$+ \frac{1}{\sqrt{\pi x}} \int_0^\infty e^{-\frac{s^2}{4x}} a(s)\, ds - \int_0^x \frac{c(s)}{\sqrt{\pi(x-s)}} ds. \quad (2.110)$$

In precisely the same way we can evaluate any one of the three functions $a(x)$, $b(x)$, $c(x)$ when the other two are known.

After substituting for $B(q)$ - as defined in (2.106) - in the expression (2.104) and translating to the original, we derive the solution of the equation (2.103)

$$u(x, y)=\frac{1}{2\sqrt{\pi y}}\int_0^\infty\left\{e^{-\frac{(x-s)^2}{4y}}+e^{-\frac{(x+s)^2}{4y}}\right\}a(s)\,ds-$$

$$-\int_0^y\frac{e^{-\frac{x^2}{4(y-t)}}}{\sqrt{\pi(y-t)}}c(t)\,dt-$$

$$-\frac{1}{2}\int_0^\infty ds\int_0^y\frac{1}{\sqrt{\pi(y-t)}}\left\{e^{-\frac{(x-s)^2}{4(y-t)}}+e^{-\frac{(x+s)^2}{4(y-t)}}\right\}f(s, t)\,dt.$$

4. Second order equations of elliptic type.

We consider Laplace's equation

$$\frac{\partial^2 u}{\partial x^2}+\frac{\partial^2 u}{\partial y^2}=0. \tag{2.111}$$

As usual we must specify the following four functions:

$$\left.\begin{aligned} u(x, 0)&=a(x)\doteqdot A(p),\\ u(0, y)&=b(y)\doteqdot B(q),\\ \left(\frac{\partial u}{\partial y}\right)_{y=0}&=a_1(x)\doteqdot A_1(p),\\ \left(\frac{\partial u}{\partial x}\right)_{x=0}&=b_1(y)\doteqdot B_1(q). \end{aligned}\right\} \tag{2.112}$$

The transformed equation has then the form

$$p^2U(p, q)-p^2B(q)-pB_1(q)+$$
$$+q^2U(p, q)-q^2A(p)-qA_1(p)=0,$$

from which it follows that

$$U(p, q)=\frac{q^2A(p)+qA_1(p)+p^2B(q)+pB_1(q)}{p^2+q^2}. \tag{2.113}$$

Since, in this case, we must take into account both zeros of the denominator, we obtain two equations of consistency for the boundary conditions:

$$q^2 A(iq) + qA_1(iq) - q^2 B(q) + iqB_1(q) = 0, \qquad (2.114)$$

$$q^2 A(-iq) + qA_1(-iq) - q^2 B(q) - iqB_1(q) = 0. \qquad (2.115)$$

In the application of the operational method we find also the solution of new problems. For example, if $a(x)$ and $a_1(x)$ are known (i.e. $A(p)$ and $A_1(p)$) then we can easily write down $B(q)$ and $B_1(q)$ from equations (2.114) and (2.115) and thus solve a problem which is not raised in the classical theory. However, if we study the classical problems of Dirichlet and Neumann by these methods we find that the elimination of two of the four functions a, b, a_1, b_1 is not always possible. Let us suppose that $a(x)$ and $b(y)$ are given (Dirichlet's problem). We would like to determine $a_1(x)$ and $b_1(y)$ in terms of these, but we encounter an immediate difficulty arising from the fact that the arguments of the function A_1 in equations (2.114) and (2.115) are different. It is therefore impossible to express the functions a_1 and b_1 independently of each other in terms of the functions a and b.

We shall not pursue further the problems originating from the application of operational methods to the solution of equations of elliptic types. For some discussion of these difficulties we refer the reader to [27] and [41].

PART TWO

Tables of Formulae

EXPLANATION OF THE TABLES OF FORMULAE

In the first table we give a list of the generally accepted notations for the special functions and some constants. The special functions and constants denoted by Latin letters are given first in alphabetical order, followed by those functions and constants denoted by Greek letters.

Then comes a list of the basic operational relations of the operational calculus of two variables. All the relations are arranged in two columns. In the left column of each page will be found image functions

$$F(p, q) = pq \int_0^\infty \int_0^\infty e^{-px-qy} f(x, y)\, dx\, dy,$$

and in the right column the corresponding original functions $f(x, y)$.

The formulæ are divided into the following sections:

Rational functions.
Irrational functions.
Exponential functions.
Logarithmic functions.
Hyperbolic and inverse hyperbolic functions.
Cylinder functions.
Integral functions.
Confluent hypergeometric functions.
Miscellaneous functions.

LIST OF NOTATIONS FOR THE SPECIAL FUNCTIONS AND SOME CONSTANTS

$$\arccos x = \frac{1}{i}\ln(x + \sqrt{x^2-1});$$

$$\arcsin x = \frac{1}{i}\ln(ix + \sqrt{1-x^2});$$

$$\operatorname{arctg} x = \frac{i}{2}\ln\frac{1-ix}{1+ix};$$

$$\operatorname{arch} x = \ln(x + \sqrt{x^2-1});$$

$$\operatorname{arsh} x = \ln(x + \sqrt{x^2+1});$$

$$\operatorname{arth} x = \frac{1}{2}\ln\frac{1+x}{1-x};$$

$$B(k) = \int_0^{\frac{\pi}{2}} \frac{\cos^2\varphi\, d\varphi}{\sqrt{1-k^2\sin^2\varphi}};$$

$$B(x, y) = \int_0^1 \xi^{x-1}(1-\xi)^{y-1}\, d\xi = \frac{\Gamma(x)\Gamma(y)}{\Gamma(x+y)};$$

$\operatorname{bei}_\nu(x) = \operatorname{Im}(J_\nu(i\sqrt{i}\,x))$,

where $\operatorname{Im}(z)$ denotes the imaginary part of the complex number z;

$\operatorname{ber}_\nu(x) = \operatorname{Re}(J_\nu(i\sqrt{i}\,x))$,

where $\operatorname{Re}(z)$ denotes the real part of the complex number z;

$$\operatorname{bei}_0(x) = \operatorname{bei} x = \operatorname{Im}[I_0(\sqrt{i}\,x)] = \sum_{n=0}^{\infty}\frac{(-1)^n}{[(2n+1)!]^2}\left(\frac{x}{2}\right)^{4n+2};$$

$$\operatorname{ber}_0(x) = \operatorname{ber} x = \operatorname{Re}[I_0(\sqrt{i}\,x)] = \sum_{n=0}^{\infty}\frac{(-1)^n}{[(2n)!]^2}\left(\frac{x}{2}\right)^{4n};$$

$$C = -\Psi(1) = 0{,}577215665\ldots;$$

$$C_n^\nu(x) = \frac{\Gamma(n+2\nu)}{\Gamma(n+1)\Gamma(2\nu)} \times {}_2F_1\left(n+2\nu, -n; \nu+\frac{1}{2}; \frac{1-x}{2}\right);$$

$$C(x) = \int_0^x \cos\frac{\pi u^2}{2}\, du = \frac{1}{2} - \sqrt{\frac{2}{\pi}}\, C^*\left(x\sqrt{\frac{\pi}{2}}\right);$$

$$C^*(x) = \int_x^\infty \cos u^2\, du = \sqrt{\frac{\pi}{2}}\left[\frac{1}{2} - C\left(x\sqrt{\frac{2}{\pi}}\right)\right];$$

continued

$$ce_{2n}(z,q)=\sum_{k=0}^{\infty}A_{2k}^{(2n)}\cos 2kz;$$

$$ce_{2n+1}(z,q)=$$
$$=\sum_{k=0}^{\infty}A_{2k+1}^{(2n+1)}\cos(2k+1)z;$$

$$Ce_{2n}(z,q)=ce_{2n}(iz,q);$$

$$Ce_{2n+1}(z,q)=ce_{2n+1}(iz,q);$$

$$\operatorname{ch} i(x)=\ln\gamma x+$$
$$+\int_0^x\frac{\operatorname{ch} u-1}{u}\,du;$$

$$\operatorname{ch} x=\frac{e^x+e^{-x}}{2};$$

$$\operatorname{ci}(x)=-\int_\infty^\infty\frac{\cos u}{u}\,du=$$
$$=\ln\gamma x-\int_0^x\frac{1-\cos u}{u}\,du;$$

$$\cos x=\frac{e^{ix}+e^{-ix}}{2};$$

$$C(k)=\int_0^{\frac{\pi}{2}}\frac{\sin^2\varphi\cos^2\varphi\,d\varphi}{(1-k^2\sin^2\varphi)^{3/2}};$$

$$D(k)=\int_0^{\frac{\pi}{2}}\frac{\sin^2\varphi\,d\varphi}{\sqrt{1-k^2\sin^2\varphi}};$$

$$D_n(x)=e^{-\frac{x^2}{4}}\operatorname{He}_n(x);$$

$$D_\nu(x)=2^{\frac{1}{4}+\frac{\nu}{2}}x^{-\frac{1}{2}}\times$$
$$\times W_{\frac{1}{4}+\frac{\nu}{2},\ \pm\frac{1}{4}}\left(\frac{x^2}{2}\right)$$

$$e=2{,}718281828\ldots;$$

$$e^x=\exp x=\sum_{n=0}^{\infty}\frac{x^n}{n!};$$

$$E(k)=\int_0^{\frac{\pi}{2}}\sqrt{1-k^2\sin^2\varphi}\,d\varphi;$$

$$E(k,\varphi)=\int_0^{\varphi}\sqrt{1-k^2\sin^2 u}\,du;$$

$$E_\nu(x)=\frac{1}{\pi}\int_0^{\pi}\sin(\nu\varphi-$$
$$-x\sin\varphi)\,d\varphi;$$

$$\operatorname{Ei}(x)=\int_{-\infty}^{x}\frac{e^u}{u}\,du=\operatorname{li}(e^x);$$

$$-\operatorname{Ei}(-x)=\int_x^{\infty}\frac{e^{-u}}{u}\,du;$$

$$\operatorname{erf}(x)=\frac{2}{\sqrt{\pi}}\int_0^x e^{-u^2}\,du;$$

$$\operatorname{erfc}(x)=1-\operatorname{erf}(x)=$$
$$=\frac{2}{\sqrt{\pi}}\int_x^{\infty}e^{-u^2}\,du;$$

$$F(k)=\int_0^{\frac{\pi}{2}}\frac{d\varphi}{\sqrt{1-k^2\sin^2\varphi}};$$

$$F(k,\varphi)=\int_0^{\varphi}\frac{du}{\sqrt{1-k^2\sin^2 u}};$$

$$F(\alpha,\beta;\gamma;x)\equiv{}_2F_1(\alpha,\beta;\gamma;x);$$

$${}_pF_q(\alpha_1, \alpha_2, \ldots, \alpha_p; \beta_1, \beta_2, \ldots, \beta_q; x) = \sum_{k=0}^{\infty} \frac{(\alpha_1, k)(\alpha_2, k)\ldots(\alpha_p, k)}{(\beta_1, k)(\beta_2, k)\ldots(\beta_q, k)} \times \frac{x^k}{k!},$$

where $(\alpha, k) = \dfrac{\Gamma(\alpha + k)}{\Gamma(\alpha)}$;

$$(\beta, k) = \frac{\Gamma(\beta + k)}{\Gamma(\beta)};$$

$$\mathfrak{F}_n(\alpha, \gamma, x) = F(-n, \alpha + n; \gamma; x) = 1 + \sum_{k=1}^{n} (-1)^k \binom{n}{k} \times \frac{(\alpha + n)\ldots(\alpha + n + k - 1)}{\gamma(\gamma + 1)\ldots(\gamma + k - 1)} x^k$$
$$(\gamma \neq 0, -1, \ldots, -n + 1);$$

$$Fek_{2n}(z, q) = \frac{ce_{2n}(0, q)}{\pi A^{(2n)}} \times \sum_{k=0}^{\infty} (-1)^k A_{2k}^{(2n)} K_{2k}(-2ik \operatorname{sh} z);$$

$$Fek_{2n+1}(z, q) = \frac{ce_{2n+1}(0, q)}{\pi k A_1^{(2n+1)}} \operatorname{cth} z \times \sum_{k=0}^{\infty} (-1)^k (2k + 1) A_{2k+1}^{(2n+1)} \times K_{2k+1}(-2ik \operatorname{sh} z);$$

$$Gek_{2n+1}(z, q) = \frac{se'_{2n+1}(0, q)}{\pi k B^{(2n+1)}} \times \sum_{k=0}^{\infty} (-1)^k B_{2k+1}^{(2n+1)} \times K_{2k+1}(-2ik \operatorname{sh} z);$$

$$Gek_{2n+2}(z, q) = -\frac{se'_{2n+2}(0, q)}{\pi k^2 B_2^{(2n+2)}} \operatorname{cth} z \times \sum_{k=0}^{\infty} (-1)^k (2k + 2) B_{2k+2}^{(2n+2)} \times K_{2k+2}(-2ik \operatorname{sh} z);$$

$$\mathbf{H}_\nu(x) = \sum_{n=0}^{\infty} \frac{(-1)^n \left(\frac{x}{2}\right)^{\nu+2n+1}}{\Gamma\left(n + \frac{3}{2}\right)\Gamma\left(n + \nu + \frac{3}{2}\right)};$$

$$H_\nu^{(1)}(x) = J_\nu(x) + iY_\nu(x);$$

$$H_\nu^{(2)}(x) = J_\nu(x) - iY_\nu(x);$$

$$He_n(x) = (-1)^n e^{\frac{x^2}{2}} \frac{d^n}{dx^n}\left(e^{-\frac{x^2}{2}}\right);$$

$$He_n^*(x) = (-1)^n e^{x^2} \frac{d^n}{dx^n}(e^{-x^2});$$

$$\operatorname{hei}_\nu(x) = \operatorname{Im}\left(H_\nu^{(1)}(i\sqrt{i}x)\right);$$

$$\operatorname{hei}_0(x) = \operatorname{hei}(x);$$

$$\operatorname{her}_\nu(x) = \operatorname{Re}\left(H_\nu^{(1)}(i\sqrt{i}x)\right);$$

$$\operatorname{her}_0(x) = \operatorname{her}(x);$$

$$I_\nu(x) = i^{-\nu} J(ix) = \sum_{k=0}^{\infty} \frac{\left(\frac{x}{2}\right)^{\nu+2x}}{k!\,\Gamma(\nu + k + 1)};$$

$$Il_\nu(x) = \int_x^{\infty} \frac{I_\nu(u)}{u} du;$$

$$J_\nu(x) = \frac{1}{\pi} \int_0^{\pi} \cos(\nu\varphi - x \sin\varphi)\, d\varphi;$$

$$J_\nu(x) = \sum_{k=0}^{\infty} \frac{(-1)^k \left(\frac{x}{2}\right)^{\nu+2k}}{k!\,\Gamma(\nu + k + 1)};$$

$$J_{\mu,\nu}(x) = \frac{x^{\mu+\nu}}{3^{\mu+\nu}\Gamma(\mu+1)\Gamma(\nu+1)} \times {}_0F_2\left(\mu+1,\ \nu+1;\ -\frac{x^3}{27}\right);$$

$$J_n^m(x) = \frac{1}{\pi}\int_0^\pi (2\cos\varphi)^m \times \cos(n\varphi - x\sin\varphi)\,d\varphi;$$

$$J_\nu(xi\sqrt{i}) = \mathrm{ber}_\nu\, x + i\,\mathrm{bei}_\nu\, x;$$

$$Jc(x, y) = \int_0^y J_0(xu)\cos u\,du;$$

$$Ji_\nu(x) = \int_x^\infty \frac{J_\nu(u)}{u}\,du;$$

$$Js(x, y) = \int_0^y J_0(xu)\sin u\,du;$$

$$K(k) = F(k);$$

$$K_\nu(x) = \frac{\pi}{2} i^{\nu+1} \mathrm{H}_\nu^{(1)}(ix);$$

$$Ki_\nu x = \int_x^\infty \frac{K_\nu(u)}{u}\,du;$$

$$\mathrm{kei}_\nu(x) = \mathrm{Im}\,(i^{-\nu}K_\nu(\sqrt{i}\,x));$$

$$\mathrm{ker}_\nu(x) = \mathrm{Re}\,(i^{-\nu}K_\nu(\sqrt{i}\,x));$$

$$\mathrm{L}_\nu(x) = i^{-\nu-1}\mathrm{H}_\nu(ix);$$

$$L_n(x) = \frac{e^x}{n!}\frac{d^n}{dx^n}(x^n e^{-x});$$

$$L_\nu(x) = \frac{e^{\frac{x}{2}}}{\sqrt{x}} M_{\nu+\frac{1}{2},\,0}(x) = {}_1F_1(-\nu;\ 1;\ x);$$

$$L_n^{(\alpha)}(x) = \frac{e^x x^{-\alpha}}{n!}\frac{d^n}{dx^n} \times (e^{-x}x^{n+\alpha});$$

$$L_\nu^{(\alpha)}(x) = \frac{\Gamma(\alpha+\nu+1)}{\Gamma(\alpha+1)\Gamma(\nu+1)} \times x^{-\frac{\alpha+1}{2}} e^{\frac{x}{2}} M_{\frac{\alpha+1}{2}+\nu,\ \frac{\alpha}{2}}(x);$$

$$\mathrm{li}\, x = \int_0^x \frac{du}{\ln u};$$

$$\ln z = i\varphi + \ln|z|,$$ где

$$z = re^{i(\varphi+2k\pi)}, \quad -\pi < \varphi < \pi;$$

$$M_{\mu,\nu}(x) = x^{\nu+\frac{1}{2}} e^{-\frac{x}{2}} \times {}_1F_1\left(\frac{1}{2}+\nu-\mu;\ 2\nu+1;\ x\right);$$

$$n! = \Pi(n) = 1\cdot 2\cdot 3\ldots n = \Gamma(n+1);$$

$$N_\nu(x) = Y_\nu(x);$$

$$N_{\mu,\nu}(x) = Y_{\mu,\nu}(x);$$

$$Ni_\nu(x) = Yi_\nu(x);$$

$$O_n(x) = \frac{1}{2}\int_0^\infty e^{-xu} \times [(u+\sqrt{u^2+1})^n + (u-\sqrt{u^2-1})^n]\,du;$$

$$P_n(x) = \frac{1}{2^n n!}\cdot\frac{d^n}{dx^n}(x^2-1)^n;$$

$$P_\nu(x) = {}_2F_1\left(-\nu,\ \nu+1;\ 1;\ \frac{1-x}{2}\right), \quad |1-x| < 2$$

$$P_\nu^m(x) = \begin{cases} (-1)^m (1-x^2)^{\frac{m}{2}} \times \dfrac{d^m P_\nu(x)}{dx^m} & \text{for } |x| \leqslant 1, \\ (x^2-1)^{\frac{m}{2}} \dfrac{d^m P_\nu(x)}{dx^m} & \text{при } |x| > 1; \end{cases}$$

and

$$Q_\nu^m(x) = (-1)^m (1-x^2)^{\frac{m}{2}} \times \frac{d^m Q_\nu(x)}{dx^m} \quad |x| \leqslant 1$$

$$Q_\nu^m(x) = (x^2-1)^{\frac{m}{2}} \times \frac{d^m Q_\nu(x)}{dx^m}, \quad |x| > 1;$$

$$P_\nu^\mu(x) = \frac{1}{\Gamma(1-\mu)} \left(\frac{x+1}{x-1}\right)^{\frac{\mu}{2}} \times {}_2F_1\left(-\nu, \nu+1; 1-\mu; \frac{1-x}{2}\right), \quad |x-1| < 2;$$

$$Q^{\nu,\rho}(x) = \sqrt{\pi}\, 2^{2\nu-1} \times \sum_{k=0}^{\infty} \frac{\Gamma(\rho+2\nu+2k)}{k!\,\Gamma(\rho+\nu+k+1)} \times (2x)^{-\rho-2\nu-2k};$$

$$P(x, \nu) = \int_0^x e^{-u} u^{\nu-1}\, du = \Gamma(\nu) - \Gamma(\nu, x) = \gamma(\nu, x);$$

$$Q(x, \nu) = \int_x^\infty e^{-u} u^{\nu-1}\, du = \Gamma(\nu, x);$$

$$Q_n(x) = \frac{1}{2^n n!} (x^2-1)^n \times \ln\frac{x+1}{x-1} - \frac{1}{2} \ln\frac{x+1}{x-1} P_n(x), \quad |x| > 1;$$

$$S(x) = \int_0^x \sin\frac{\pi u^2}{2}\, du = \frac{1}{2} - \sqrt{\frac{2}{\pi}}\, S^*\left(x\sqrt{\frac{\pi}{2}}\right);$$

$$Q_\nu(x) = \frac{\sqrt{\pi}}{2^{\nu+1}} \frac{\Gamma(\nu+1)}{\Gamma\left(\nu+\frac{3}{2}\right)} x^{-\nu-1} \times {}_2F_1\left(\frac{\nu}{2}+1, \frac{\nu+1}{2}; \nu+\frac{3}{2}; \frac{1}{x^2}\right);$$

$$S^*(x) = \int_x^\infty \sin u^2\, du = \sqrt{\frac{\pi}{2}}\left[\frac{1}{2} - S\left(x\sqrt{\frac{2}{\pi}}\right)\right];$$

$$Q_\nu^\mu(x) = e^{\pi i \mu} \frac{\sqrt{\pi}}{2^{\nu+1}} \frac{\Gamma(\nu+\mu+1)}{\Gamma\left(\nu+\frac{3}{2}\right)} \times (x^2-1)^{\frac{\mu}{2}} x^{-\mu-\nu-1} \times {}_2F_1\left(\frac{\mu+\nu}{2}+1, \frac{\mu+\nu+1}{2}; \nu+\frac{3}{2}; \frac{1}{x^2}\right);$$

$$S(\nu, x) = \int_0^\infty \frac{e^{-xu}\, du}{(1+u)^\nu} = x^{\nu-1} e^x \int_x^\infty e^{-\xi} \xi^{-\nu}\, d\xi;$$

$$s_1(x) = \frac{1}{3}(e^{-x} + e^{-\varepsilon x} + e^{-\varepsilon^2 x});$$

$$s_2(x) = \frac{1}{3}(e^{-x} + \varepsilon e^{-\varepsilon x} + \varepsilon^2 e^{-\varepsilon^2 x});$$

$$s_3(x) = \frac{1}{3}(e^{-x} + \varepsilon^2 e^{-\varepsilon x} + \varepsilon e^{-\varepsilon^2 x}), \quad \varepsilon \neq 1 \text{ и } \varepsilon^3 = 1;$$

$$S_n(x) = \int_0^\infty e^{-xu} \times [(u + \sqrt{u^2+1})^n - (u - \sqrt{u^2+1})^n] \frac{du}{\sqrt{u^2+1}};$$

$$se_{2n+1}(z, q) = \sum_{k=0}^{\infty} B_{2k+1}^{(2n+1)} \sin(2k+1) z;$$

$$se_{2n}(z, q) = \sum_{k=1}^{\infty} B_{2k}^{(2n)} \sin(2k) z;$$

$$Se_{2n}(z, q) = -i se_{2n}(iz, q);$$

$$Se_{2n+1}(z, q) = -i se_{2n+1}(iz, q);$$

$$\operatorname{sh} x = \frac{e^x - e^{-x}}{2};$$

$$\operatorname{shi} x = \int_0^x \frac{\operatorname{sh} u}{u} du;$$

$$\operatorname{si}(x) = -\int_x^\infty \frac{\sin u}{u} du;$$

$$\operatorname{Si}(x) = \int_0^x \frac{\sin u}{u} du = \frac{\pi}{2} + \operatorname{si}(x);$$

$$\sin(x) = \frac{e^{ix} - e^{-ix}}{2};$$

$$\operatorname{stei}_\nu(x) = \operatorname{Im}(\mathrm{H}_\nu(i\sqrt{ix}));$$

$$\operatorname{ster}_\nu(x) = \operatorname{Re}(\mathrm{H}_\nu(i\sqrt{ix}));$$

$$s_{\mu,\nu}(x) = \frac{x^{\mu+1}}{(\mu+\nu+1)(\mu-\nu+1)} \times {}_1F_2\left(1; \frac{\mu+\nu+3}{2}; \frac{\mu-\nu+3}{2}; -\frac{x^2}{4}\right);$$

$$S_{\mu,\nu}(x) = s_{\mu,\nu}(x) + 2^{\mu-1} \times \Gamma\left(\frac{\mu-\nu+1}{2}\right)\Gamma\left(\frac{\mu+\nu+1}{2}\right) \times \frac{1}{\sin \nu\pi}\left[\cos\left(\frac{\mu-\nu}{2}\pi\right) J_{-\nu}(x) - \cos\left(\frac{\mu+\nu}{2}\pi\right) J_{-\nu}(x)\right];$$

$$T_n(x) = \cos(n \arccos x) = \frac{1}{2}[(x + \sqrt{x^2-1})^n + (x - \sqrt{x^2-1})^n];$$

$$T_\alpha^{(n)}(x) = (-1)^n \frac{L_n^{(\alpha)}(x)}{\Gamma(\alpha+n+1)};$$

$$U(x, \alpha) = \frac{1}{\sqrt{\pi x}} \times \left[1 + 2\sum_{k=1}^{\infty} e^{-2k\alpha - \frac{k^2}{x}}\right];$$

$$U_n(x) = \sin(n \arccos x) = \frac{1}{2i}[(x + \sqrt{x^2-1})^n - (x - \sqrt{x^2-1})^n];$$

$$U_\nu(w, x) = \sum_{m=0}^{\infty} (-1)^m \times \left(\frac{w}{x}\right)^{\nu+2m} \times J_{\nu+2m}(x);$$

$$V_\nu(w, x) = \sum_{m=0}^{\infty} (-1)^m \times \left(\frac{w}{x}\right)^{-\nu-2m} \times J_{-\nu-2m}(x);$$

$$W_{\mu,\nu}(x) = \frac{\Gamma(-2\nu)}{\Gamma\left(\frac{1}{2}-\mu-\nu\right)} \times M_{\mu,\nu}(x) + \frac{\Gamma(2\nu)}{\Gamma\left(\frac{1}{2}-\mu+\nu\right)} \times M_{\mu,-\nu}(x);$$

$$Y_\nu(x) = \frac{\cos \nu\pi J_\nu(x) - J_{-\nu}(x)}{\sin \nu\pi};$$

$$Yl_\nu(x) = \int_x^\infty \frac{Y_\nu(u)}{u}\, du;$$

$$Y_{\mu,\nu}(x) = \frac{x^{\nu-\frac{1}{2}}}{\Gamma(2\nu+1)} M_{\mu,\nu}(x);$$

$$[x] = n \text{ for } n \leqslant x < n+1;$$

$$(x) = x - [x];$$

$$\gamma = e^C = 1{,}781072\ldots;$$

$$\Gamma(x) = \int_0^\infty u^{x-1} e^{-u}\, du = \Pi(x-1);$$

$$\Gamma(\nu, x) = \int_x^\infty u^{\nu-1} e^{-u}\, du = Q(x, \nu);$$

$$\gamma(\nu, x) = \Gamma(\nu) - \Gamma(\nu, x) = P(x, \nu);$$

$$\zeta(x) = \sum_{n=1}^{\infty} \frac{1}{n^x};$$

$$\zeta(x, \nu) = \sum_{n=0}^{\infty} \frac{1}{(n+\nu)^x};$$

$$\vartheta_0(v, x) = 1 + 2\sum_{k=1}^{\infty} (-1)^k \times e^{-\pi^2 k^2 x} \cos 2\pi k v;$$

$$\vartheta_1(v, x) = 2\sum_{k=0}^{\infty} (-1)^k \times e^{-\pi^2\left(k+\frac{1}{2}\right)^2 x} \sin \pi(2k+1) v;$$

$$\vartheta_2(v, x) = 2\sum_{k=0}^{\infty} e^{-\pi^2\left(k+\frac{1}{2}\right)^2 x} \times \cos \pi(2k+1) v$$

$$\vartheta_3(v, x) = 1 + 2\sum_{k=1}^{\infty} e^{-\pi^2 k^2 x} \cos 2\pi k v$$

$$\hat{\vartheta}_0(v, x) = \frac{1}{\sqrt{\pi x}}\left[\sum_{k=0}^{\infty} e^{-\frac{1}{x}\left(v+k+\frac{1}{2}\right)^2} - \sum_{k=-1}^{-\infty} e^{-\frac{1}{x}\left(v+k+\frac{1}{2}\right)^2}\right]$$

$$\hat{\vartheta}_1(v, x) = \frac{1}{\sqrt{\pi x}} \times \left[\sum_{k=0}^{\infty} (-1)^k e^{-\frac{1}{x}\left(v+k-\frac{1}{2}\right)^2} - \sum_{k=-1}^{-\infty} (-1)^k e^{-\frac{1}{x}\left(v+k-\frac{1}{2}\right)^2}\right]$$

$$\hat{\vartheta}_2(v, x) = \frac{1}{\sqrt{\pi x}} \times \left[\sum_{k=0}^{\infty} (-1)^k e^{-\frac{1}{x}(v+k)^2} - \sum_{k=-1}^{-\infty} (-1)^k e^{-\frac{1}{x}(v+k)^2}\right]$$

$$\vartheta_3(v, x) = \frac{1}{\sqrt{\pi x}} \times \left[\sum_{k=0}^{\infty} e^{-\frac{1}{x}(v+k)^2} - \sum_{k=-1}^{-\infty} e^{-\frac{1}{x}(v+k)^2} \right];$$

$$\vartheta_n(w, x) = i^{-n} V_n(iw, ix);$$

$$\lambda(e^x, \alpha) = \int_0^{\alpha} e^{-xu} \Gamma(u+1)\, du;$$

$$\Lambda(n) = \begin{cases} \ln q & \text{for } n = q^m, \text{ where } q \text{ is a prime number and } m > 0, \\ 0 & \text{otherwise}; \end{cases}$$

$$\mu(x, a) = \int_0^{\infty} \frac{x^u u^a}{\Gamma(u+1)}\, du;$$

$$(x, a, b) = \int_0^{\infty} \frac{x^{u+b} u^a}{\Gamma(u+b+1)}\, du;$$

$$\nu(x) = \int_0^{\infty} \frac{x^u\, du}{\Gamma(u+1)} = \int_1^{\infty} \frac{x^{u-1}\, du}{\Gamma(u)};$$

$$\nu(x, a) = \int_a^{\infty} \frac{x^u\, du}{\Gamma(u+1)};$$

$$\nu l(x, a) = \int_0^{x} \frac{\nu(u, a)}{u}\, du;$$

$$\Upsilon_n(w, x) = i^{-n} U_n(iw, ix);$$

$$\Pi(x) = \Gamma(x+1),$$

$$\pi = 3{,}14159265 \ldots;$$

$$\varphi(x) = \sum_{n \leqslant x} \Lambda(n), \quad x \geqslant 0;$$

$$\psi(x, y) = \frac{x}{2\sqrt{\pi y^3}} e^{-\frac{x^2}{4y}};$$

$$\Psi(x) = \frac{\Gamma'(x)}{\Gamma(x)};$$

$$\omega(x) = \ln \Gamma(x) - \left(x - \frac{1}{2}\right) \ln x + x - \ln \sqrt{2\pi};$$

$$\chi(x, y) = \frac{1}{\sqrt{\pi y}} e^{-\frac{x^2}{4y}}.$$

LIST OF FUNDAMENTAL OPERATIONAL RELATIONS

№	$F(p, q)$	$f(x, y)$
0	$pq \dfrac{\partial^n}{\partial p^n}\left[\dfrac{F(p, q)}{pq}\right]$	$(-x)^n f(x, y)$
1	$pq \dfrac{\partial^2}{\partial p\, \partial q}\left[\dfrac{F(p, q)}{pq}\right]$	$xy f(x, y)$
2	$pq \dfrac{\partial^{m+n}}{\partial p^m\, \partial q^n}\left[\dfrac{F(p, q)}{pq}\right]$	$(-x)^m (-y)^n f(x, y)$
3	$p \dfrac{\partial F(p, q)}{\partial p}$	$-x \dfrac{\partial f(x, y)}{\partial x}$
4	$pq \dfrac{\partial^2 F(p, q)}{\partial p\, \partial q}$	$xy \dfrac{\partial^2 f(x, y)}{\partial x\, \partial y}$
5	$pq \dfrac{\partial^{m+n}}{\partial p^m\, \partial q^n} F(p, q)$	$(-x)^m (-y)^n \dfrac{\partial^2 f(x, y)}{\partial x\, \partial y}$
6	$p^r q^s \dfrac{\partial^{m+n} F(p, q)}{\partial p^m\, \partial q^n}$ r, s, m, n — positive integers $m \geqslant r,\ n \geqslant s$	$\dfrac{\partial^{r+s-2}}{\partial x^{r-1}\, \partial y^{s-1}} \times$ $\times \Big[(-x)^m (-y)^n \dfrac{\partial^2 f(x, y)}{\partial x\, \partial y}\Big]$
7	$pq \dfrac{\partial^{r+s}}{\partial p^r\, \partial q^s}\left[p^{m-1} q^{n-1} F(p, q)\right]$ r, s, m, n — positive integers $r \geqslant m,\ s \geqslant n$	$(-x)^r (-y)^s \dfrac{\partial^{m+n} f(x, y)}{\partial x^m\, \partial y^n}$

continued

№	$F(p, q)$	$f(x, y)$
8	$\dfrac{\partial^{m+n-2}}{\partial p^{m-1}\,\partial q^{n-1}}\left[p^m q^n \dfrac{\partial^2 F(p, q)}{\partial p\,\partial q}\right]$ r, s, m, n — positive integers $r \geqslant m$, $s \geqslant n$	$(-x)^m(-y)^n \dfrac{\partial^{m+n} f(x, y)}{\partial x^m\,\partial y^n}$
9	$pF(p, q) - pF_2(0, q)$ *	$\dfrac{\partial}{\partial x} f(x, y)$
10	$qF(p, q) - qF_1(p, 0)$	$\dfrac{\partial}{\partial y} f(x, y)$
11	$p^2F(p, q) - p^2F_2(0, q) - pF_{2, x}(0, q)$	$\dfrac{\partial^2}{\partial x^2} f(x, y)$
12	$pqF(p, q) - pqF_2(0, q) - pqF_1(p, 0) + pqf(0, 0)$	$\dfrac{\partial^2}{\partial x\,\partial y} f(x, y)$
13	$q^2F(p, q) - q^2F_1(p, 0) - qF_{1, y}(p, 0)$	$\dfrac{\partial^2}{\partial y^2} f(x, y)$

* We adopt the following notation throughout:

$$F_1(p, y) = p \int_0^\infty e^{-p\xi} f(\xi, y)\, d\xi,$$

$$F_2(x, q) = q \int_0^\infty e^{-q\eta} f(x, \eta)\, d\eta,$$

$$F_{1, y^l}(p, 0) = p \int_0^\infty e^{-p\xi} \left.\frac{\partial^l f(\xi, y)}{\partial y^l}\right|_{y=0} d\xi,$$

$$F_{2, x^k}(0, q) = q \int_0^\infty e^{-q\eta} \left.\frac{\partial^k f(x, \eta)}{\partial x^k}\right|_{x=0} d\eta,$$

continued

№	$F(p, q)$	$f(x, y)$
14	$p^3F(p, q) - p^3F_2(0, q) - p^2F_{2, x}(0, q) - pF_{2, xx}(0, q)$	$\frac{\partial^3}{\partial x^3} f(x, y)$
15	$p^2qF(p, q) - p^2qF_2(0, q) - p^2qF_1(p, 0) + p^2qf(0, 0) - pqF_{2, x}(0, q) + pqf'_x(0, 0)$	$\frac{\partial^3}{\partial x^2\, \partial y} f(x, y)$
16	$pq^2F(p, q) - pq^2F_1(p, 0) - pq^2F_2(0, q) + pq^2f(0, 0) - pqF_{1, y}(p, 0) + pqf'_y(0, 0)$	$\frac{\partial^3}{\partial x\, \partial y^2} f(x, y)$
17	$q^3F(p, q) - q^3F_1(p, 0) - q^2F_{1, y}(p, 0) - qF_{1, yy}(p, 0)$	$\frac{\partial_3}{\partial y^3} f(x, y)$
18	$p^4F(p, q) - p^4F_2(0, q) - p^3F_{2, x}(0, q) - p^2F_{2, xx}(0, q) - pF_{2, xxx}(0, q)$	$\frac{\partial^4}{\partial x^4} f(x, y)$
19	$p^3qF(p, q) - p^3qF_1(p, 0) - p^3qF_2(0, q) - p^2qF_{2, x}(0, q) - pqF_{2, xx}(0, q) + p^3qf(0, 0) + p^2qf'_x(0, 0) + pqf''_{xx}(0, 0)$	$\frac{\partial^4}{\partial x^3\, \partial y} f(x, y)$
20	$p^2q^2F(p, q) - p^2q^2F_1(p, 0) - p^2q^2F_2(0, q) - p^2qF_{1, y}(p, 0) - pq^2F_{2, x}(0, q) + p^2q^2f(0, 0) + p^2qf'_y(0, 0) + pq^2f'_x(0, 0) + pqf''_{xy}(0, 0)$	$\frac{\partial^4}{\partial x^2\, \partial y^2} f(x, y)$
21	$pq^3F(p, q) - pq^3F_2(0, q) - pq^3F_1(p, 0) - pq^2F_{1, y}(p, 0) - pqF_{1, yy}(p, 0) + pq^3f(0, 0) + pq^2f'_y(0, 0) + pqf''_{yy}(0, 0)$	$\frac{\partial^4}{\partial x\, \partial y^3} f(x, y)$
22	$q^4F(p, q) - q^4F_1(p, 0) - q^3F_{1, y}(p, 0) - q^2F_{1, yy}(p, 0) - qF_{1, yyy}(p, 0)$	$\frac{\partial^4}{\partial y^4} f(x, y)$
23	$p^nF(p, q) - \sum_{k=0}^{n-1} p^{n-k}F_{2, x^k}(0, q)$ $(n \geqslant 1)$	$\frac{\partial^n}{\partial x^n} f(x, y)$

continued

№	$F(p, q)$	$f(x, y)$
24	$q^n F(p, q) - \sum_{k=0}^{n-1} q^{n-k} F_{1, y^k}(p, 0)$ $(n \geqslant 1)$	$\frac{\partial^n}{\partial y^n} f(x, y)$
25	$p^m q^n F(p, q) - p^m \sum_{l=0}^{n-1} q^{n-l} F_{1, y^l}(p, 0) - q^n \sum_{k=0}^{m-1} p^{m-k} F_{2, x^k}(0, q) + \sum_{k=0}^{m-1} \sum_{l=0}^{n-1} p^{m-k} q^{n-l} f^{(k+l)}_{x^k y^l}(0, 0)$	$\frac{\partial^{m+n}}{\partial x^m \partial y^n} f(x, y)$ $(m, n \geqslant 1)$
26	$\frac{pq}{\pi} \int_0^\infty \int_0^\infty e^{-\frac{p^2\lambda^2}{4} - \frac{q^2\mu^2}{4}} \times \frac{\lambda^2 F\left(\frac{1}{\lambda^2}\right) - \mu^2 F\left(\frac{1}{\mu^2}\right)}{\lambda^2 - \mu^2} \, d\lambda \, d\mu$	$f(x^2 + y^2)$
27	$-pq \int_0^{\frac{\pi}{2}} \Phi'(p \cos \theta + q \sin \theta) \, d\theta$ *	$f(\sqrt{x^2 + y^2})$
28	$pq \int_0^{\frac{\pi}{2}} \Phi(p \cos \theta + q \sin \theta) \, d\theta$	$\frac{f(\sqrt{x^2 + y^2})}{\sqrt{x^2 + y^2}}$
29	$pq \int_0^{\frac{\pi}{2}} \Phi(p \cos \theta + q \sin \theta + a) \, d\theta$	$e^{-a\sqrt{x^2+y^2}} \frac{f(\sqrt{x^2+y^2})}{\sqrt{x^2+y^2}}$

* The expression for the function Φ is given on p.62

continued

№	$F(p, q)$	$f(x, y)$
30	$pq \int_0^{\frac{\pi}{2}} \frac{\Phi(\text{tg}\,\theta)}{(p\cos\theta + q\sin\theta)^2}\, d\theta$	$f\left(\frac{y}{x}\right)$
31	$pq \int_0^{\frac{\pi}{2}} \frac{\Phi(\text{tg}\,\theta)}{p\cos\theta + q\sin\theta}\, d\theta$	$\frac{f\left(\frac{y}{x}\right)}{\sqrt{x^2+y^2}}$
32	$\frac{p}{p+a} \cdot \frac{q}{q+b} F(p+a, q+b)$	$e^{-ax-by} f(x, y)$
33	$\frac{F(p)-F(q)}{p-q}$	$\int_0^x f(\xi)\, d\xi + \int_0^y f(\eta)\, d\eta + \int_0^{x+y} f(\xi)\, d\xi$
34	$-\frac{qF(p)-pF(q)}{p-q}$	$f(x+y)$
35	$pq\left\{-\frac{F(p)-F(q)}{p-q}\right\}$	$f'(x+y)$
36	$pq\left[-\frac{pF(p)-qF(q)}{p-q}+f(0)\right]$	$f''(x+y)$
37	$pq\left\{-\frac{p^2F(p)-q^2F(q)}{p-q}\right\} + pq\{f'(0)+(p+q)f(0)\}$	$f'''(x+y)$

continued

№	$F(p, q)$	$f(x, y)$
38	$pq\left\{-\dfrac{p^3F(p)-q^3F(q)}{p-q}\right\}+$ $+pq\{f''(0)+(p+q)f'(0)+$ $+(p^2+pq+q^2)f(0)\}$	$f^{IV}(x+y)$
39	$pq\left\{-\dfrac{p^{n-1}F(p)-q^{n-1}F(q)}{p-q}\right\}+$ $+pq\{(p^{n-2}+p^{n-3}q+\ldots+pq^{n-3}+q^{n-2})f(0)+$ $+(p^{n-3}+p^{n-4}q+\ldots+pq^{n-4}+q^{n-3})f'(0)+$ $+(p^{n-4}+p^{n-5}q+\ldots+pq^{n-5}+q^{n-4})f''(0)+$ . . . . $+(p+q)f^{(n-3)}(0)+f^{(n-2)}(0)\}$	$f^{(n)}(x+y)$
40	$e^{pa}\left\{F(p, q)-p\int\limits_0^a e^{-p\xi}F_2(\xi, q)\,d\xi\right\}$ $a\geqslant 0$	$f(x+a, y)$
41	$e^{pa+qb}\left\{F(p, q)-p\int\limits_0^a e^{-p\xi}F_2(\xi, q)\,d\xi-\right.$ $-q\int\limits_0^b e^{-q\eta}F_1(p, \eta)\,d\eta+$ $\left.+pq\int\limits_0^a\int\limits_0^b e^{-p\xi-q\eta}f(\xi, \eta)\,d\xi\,d\eta\right\}$ $a, b\geqslant 0$	$f(x+a, y+b)$
42	$(e^{ap}-1)F(p, q)-pe^{ap}\int\limits_0^a e^{-p\lambda}F_2(\lambda, q)\,d\lambda$	$\Delta_{a, x}f(x, y)=$ $=f(x+a, y)-$ $-f(x, y)$

continued

№	$F(p, q)$	$f(x, y)$
43	$(e^{ap}-1)(e^{bq}-1)F(p,q)-$ $-(e^{ap}-1)qe^{bq}\int_0^b e^{-q\mu}F_1(p,\mu)\,d\mu-$ $-(e^{bq}-1)pe^{ap}\int_0^a e^{-p\lambda}F_2(\lambda,q)\,d\lambda+$ $+pqe^{ap+bq}\int_0^a\int_0^b e^{-p\lambda-q\mu}f(\lambda,\mu)\,d\lambda\,d\mu$	$\Delta_{a,x}\Delta_{b,y}f(x,y)=$ $=f(x+a,y+b)-$ $-f(x+a,y)-$ $-f(x,y+b)+$ $+f(x,y)$
44	$\frac{pq}{pq+1}F\left(p+\frac{1}{q}\right)$	$J_0(2\sqrt{xy})f(x)$
45	$\frac{p\sqrt{q}}{p+\sqrt{q}}F(p+\sqrt{q})$	$\chi(x,y)f(x)$
46	$\frac{1}{2}p\int_0^\infty \chi(p,\lambda)F(\lambda,q)\frac{d\lambda}{\lambda}$	$f(x^2,y)$
47	$\frac{1}{4}pq\int_0^\infty\int_0^\infty \chi(p,\lambda)\chi(q,\mu)F(\lambda,\mu)\frac{d\lambda\,d\mu}{\lambda\mu}$	$f(x^2,y^2)$
48	$\frac{pqF\left(p+q+\frac{a}{q}\right)}{pq+q^2+a}$	$\begin{cases} J_0(2\sqrt{a(y-x)x})f(x) & \text{for } y>x \\ 0 & \text{for } y<x \end{cases}$
49	$\frac{1}{2}p\int_0^\infty \psi(p,\lambda)F(\lambda,q)\frac{d\lambda}{\lambda}$	$xf(x^2,y)$
50	$\frac{pF(ap+bq+c)}{ap+bq+c}$	$\begin{cases} \frac{1}{a}e^{-\frac{c}{a}x}f\left(\frac{x}{a}\right) & \text{for } y>\frac{b}{a}x \\ 0 & \text{for } y<\frac{b}{a}x \end{cases}$

continued

№	$F(p, q)$	$f(x, y)$
51	$\frac{1}{4} pq \int_0^\infty \int_0^\infty \psi(p, \lambda)\psi(q, \mu) F(\lambda, \mu) \frac{d\lambda\, d\mu}{\lambda\mu}$	$xyf(x^2, y^2)$
52	$\int_0^\infty \sqrt{\frac{p}{\lambda}} J_1(2\sqrt{p\lambda}) F(\lambda, q)\, d\lambda$	$f\left(\frac{1}{x}, y\right)$
53	$\int_0^\infty \int_0^\infty \sqrt{\frac{pq}{\lambda\mu}} J_1(2\sqrt{p\lambda}) J_1(2\sqrt{q\mu}) \times$ $\times F(\lambda, \mu)\, d\lambda\, d\mu$	$f\left(\frac{1}{x}, \frac{1}{y}\right)$
54	$p \int_0^\infty J_0(2\sqrt{p\lambda}) F(\lambda, q) \frac{d\lambda}{\lambda}$	$\frac{1}{x} \cdot f\left(\frac{1}{x}, y\right)$
55	$\int_0^\infty \left(\frac{\lambda}{p}\right)^{\frac{\alpha}{2}-1} J_\alpha(2\sqrt{p\lambda}) F(\lambda, q)\, d\lambda$	$x^{\alpha-1} f\left(\frac{1}{x}, y\right)$
56	$pq \int_0^\infty \int_0^\infty J_0(2\sqrt{p\lambda}) J_0(2\sqrt{q\mu}) \times$ $\times F(\lambda, \mu) \frac{d\lambda\, d\mu}{\lambda\mu}$	$\frac{1}{xy} \cdot f\left(\frac{1}{x}, \frac{1}{y}\right)$
57	$\int_0^\infty \int_0^\infty \left(\frac{\lambda}{p}\right)^{\frac{\alpha}{2}-1} \left(\frac{\mu}{q}\right)^{\frac{\beta}{2}-1} J_\alpha(2\sqrt{p\lambda}) \times$ $\times J_\beta(2\sqrt{q\mu}) F(\lambda, \mu)\, d\lambda\, d\mu$	$x^{\alpha-1} y^{\beta-1} f\left(\frac{1}{x}, \frac{1}{y}\right)$

continued

№	$F(p, q)$	$f(x, y)$
58	$\frac{1}{\pi}\int_0^\infty\int_0^\infty\left(\frac{\sin 2\sqrt{p\lambda}}{2\sqrt{p}}-\sqrt{\lambda}\cos 2\sqrt{p\lambda}\right)\times\left(\frac{\sin 2\sqrt{q\mu}}{2\sqrt{q}}-\sqrt{\mu}\cos 2\sqrt{q\mu}\right)\times F(\lambda, \mu)\frac{d\lambda\, d\mu}{\lambda\mu}$	$\sqrt{xy}\, f\left(\frac{1}{x}, \frac{1}{y}\right)$
59	$pq\int_0^\infty\int_0^\infty \frac{e^{-\frac{p}{\lambda}-\frac{q}{\mu}}}{(\lambda\mu)^{\frac{5}{2}}}\cdot f(\lambda, \mu)\, d\lambda\, d\mu$	$\sqrt{xy} f\left(\frac{1}{x}, \frac{1}{y}\right)$
60	$p\int_p^\infty e^{-(\lambda-p)}F(\lambda, q)\frac{d\lambda}{\lambda}$	$\frac{1}{x+1}f(x, y)$
61	$\int_p^\infty \frac{pq}{q+\lambda-p}F(\lambda, q+\lambda-p)\frac{d\lambda}{\lambda}$	$\frac{1}{x+y}f(x, y)$
62	$p\int_p^\infty \frac{F(\lambda, q)}{\lambda}\, d\lambda$	$\frac{1}{x}f(x, y)$
63	$pq\int_p^\infty\int_q^\infty \frac{F(\lambda, \mu)}{\lambda\mu}\, d\lambda\, d\mu$	$\frac{f(x, y)}{xy}$
64	$\int_0^p \frac{F(\lambda, q)}{\lambda}\, d\lambda$	$\int_x^\infty \frac{f(\xi, y)}{\xi}\, d\xi$

continued

№	$F(p, q)$	$f(x, y)$
65	$\int_0^p \int_0^q \frac{F(\lambda, \mu)}{\lambda\mu} \, d\lambda \, d\mu$	$\int_x^\infty \int_y^\infty \frac{f(\xi, \eta)}{\xi\eta} \, d\xi \, d\eta$
66	$\int_0^\infty \frac{F(\lambda, q)}{\lambda} \, d\lambda$	$\int_0^\infty \frac{f(\xi, y)}{\xi} \, d\xi$
67	$\int_0^\infty \int_0^\infty \frac{F(\lambda, \mu)}{\lambda\mu} \, d\lambda \, d\mu$	$\int_0^\infty \int_0^\infty \frac{f(\xi, \eta)}{\xi\eta} \, d\xi \, d\eta$
68	$\frac{1}{pq} F_1(p, q) F_2(p, q)$	$\int_0^x \int_0^y f_1(\xi, \eta) \times$ $\times f_2(x-\xi, y-\eta) \, d\xi \, d\eta$

TABLES

RATIONAL FUNCTIONS

№	$F(p, q)$	$f(x, y)$
1.1	1	1
1.2	$\frac{pq}{(p-a)(q-b)}$	e^{ax+by}
1.3	$\frac{1}{p^m q^n}$	$\frac{x^m y^n}{m!n!}$
1.4	$\frac{q}{p+q-b}$	$\begin{cases} 0 & \text{for } y > x, \\ e^{by} & \text{for } y < x \end{cases}$
1.5	$\frac{pq}{(p-a)(p+q-a)}$	$\begin{cases} 0 & \text{for } y > x, \\ e^{ax} & \text{for } y < x \end{cases}$
1.6	$\frac{pq}{pq+a}$	$J_0(2\sqrt{axy})$
1.7	$\frac{pq}{p^2q^2-a}$	$I_0(2\sqrt{axy})$
1.8	$\frac{pq}{p^2q^2+1}$	$\text{bei}\,(2\sqrt{xy})$
1.9	$\frac{p^2q^2}{p^2q^2+1}$	$\text{ber}\,(2\sqrt{xy})$
1.10	$\frac{pq}{pq-ap-bq+c}$	$e^{bx+ay}J_0(2\sqrt{(c-ab)xy})$

continued

№	$F(p, q)$	$f(x, y)$
1.11	$\dfrac{pq}{p^2+apq+b}$ $a>0$	$\begin{cases} 0 & \text{for } y>ax, \\ \dfrac{1}{a} J_0\left(\dfrac{2}{a}\sqrt{by(ax-y)}\right) & \text{for } y<ax \end{cases}$
1.12	$\dfrac{pq}{(p+aq+b)(p+\alpha q+d)+c}$ $0\leqslant\alpha<a$	$\begin{cases} \dfrac{1}{a-\alpha} e^{-b\frac{y-\alpha x}{a-\alpha}-d\frac{ax-y}{a-\alpha}} \times \\ \times J_0\left(\dfrac{2}{a-\alpha}\sqrt{c(y-\alpha x)(ax-y)}\right) \\ \text{for } \alpha x<y<ax, \\ 0 \text{ otherwise} \end{cases}$
1.13	$\dfrac{pq}{ap^2+2bpq+cq^2+ +2du+2eq+f}$ $b^2>ac$	$\begin{cases} \dfrac{1}{2D} e^{-\frac{1}{D^2}[(be-cd)x-(bd-ae\ y]} \times \\ \times J_0\left(\dfrac{1}{D^2}\sqrt{cx^2-2bxy+ay^2} \times \right. \\ \left. \times \sqrt{acf+2bde-b^2f-ae^2-cd^2)}\right) \\ \text{for } (b-D)x<ay<(b+D)x, \\ 0 \text{ otherwise} \end{cases}$ $D=\sqrt{b^2-ac}$
1.14	$\dfrac{pq}{(p+q)(p-1)(q-1)}$	$\begin{cases} e^y \operatorname{sh} x & \text{for } y>x, \\ e^x \operatorname{sh} y & \text{for } y<x \end{cases}$
1.15	$\dfrac{pq}{(p-1)(q-1)(p+q-1)}$	$\begin{cases} e^y(e^x-1) & \text{for } y>x, \\ e^x(e^y-1) & \text{for } y<x \end{cases}$
1.16	$\dfrac{pq}{pq(p+q+a)}$ $a\neq 0$	$\begin{cases} \dfrac{1-e^{-ax}}{a} & \text{for } y>x, \\ \dfrac{1-e^{-ay}}{a} & \text{for } y<x \end{cases}$

continued

№	$F(p, q)$	$f(x, y)$
1.17	$\dfrac{pq}{p^2q+a}$ $a \neq 0$	$\sqrt{\pi}\,\dfrac{x}{2}\left(\dfrac{4}{ax^2y}\right)^{\frac{1}{6}} J_{0,\frac{1}{2}}\left(3\sqrt[3]{\dfrac{ax^2y}{4}}\right) = x\,{}_0F_2\left(1, \dfrac{3}{2}; -\dfrac{ax^2y}{4}\right)$
1.18	$\dfrac{q}{pq+a}$ $a \neq 0$	$-\dfrac{1}{a}\dfrac{\partial}{\partial y} J_0(2\sqrt{axy}) = \sqrt{\dfrac{x}{ay}}\, J_1(2\sqrt{axy})$
1.19	$\dfrac{q^2}{(p+q)(p+2q)}$	$\begin{cases} -\dfrac{1}{2} & \text{for } x<y<2x, \\ \dfrac{1}{2} & \text{for } 0<y<x \end{cases}$
1.20	$\dfrac{pq}{(p+aq+b)[(p+aq+b)\times(p+\alpha q+d)+c]}$ $0 \leqslant \alpha < a$	$\begin{cases} \dfrac{1}{a-\alpha} e^{-b\frac{y-\alpha x}{a-\alpha}-d\frac{ax-y}{a-\alpha}} \times \sqrt{\dfrac{y-\alpha x}{c(ax-y)}} \times J_1\left(\dfrac{2}{a-\alpha}\sqrt{c(y-\alpha x)(ax-y)}\right) \\ \text{for } \alpha x<y<ax, \\ 0 \text{ otherwise} \end{cases}$
1.21	$\dfrac{1}{p^{\nu}}\,\dfrac{pq}{1+p^2q^2}$	$\left(\dfrac{x}{y}\right)^{\frac{1}{2}\nu}\left[\operatorname{bei}_{\nu}(2\sqrt{xy})\cos\dfrac{3\nu\pi}{4} - \operatorname{ber}_{\nu}(2\sqrt{xy})\sin\dfrac{3\nu\pi}{4}\right]$
1.22	$\dfrac{p^2q}{p^2q+a}$	$\sqrt{\pi}\left(\dfrac{ax^2y}{4}\right)^{\frac{1}{6}} J_{0,-\frac{1}{2}}\left(3\sqrt[3]{\dfrac{ax^2y}{4}}\right) = {}_0F_2\left(\dfrac{1}{2}, 1; -\dfrac{ax^2y}{4}\right)$

continued

№	$F(p, q)$	$f(x, y)$
1.23	$\dfrac{p+q}{p+q-1}$	$\begin{cases} e^x & \text{for } y > x, \\ e^y & \text{for } y < x \end{cases}$
1.24	$\dfrac{pq(p+q-2)}{(p-1)(q-1)(p+q-1)}$	$\begin{cases} e^y & \text{for } y > x, \\ e^x & \text{for } y < x \end{cases}$
1.25	$\dfrac{pq(bp+aq)}{(p-a)(q-b)\times \times(bp+aq-ab)}$ $\dfrac{a}{b} \geqslant 0$	$\begin{cases} e^{by}(2e^{ax}-1) & \text{for } y > \dfrac{a}{b}x, \\ e^{ax}(2e^{by}-1) & \text{for } y < \dfrac{a}{b}x \end{cases}$
1.26	$\dfrac{p}{q(p+aq)^2}$ $a \geqslant 0$	$\begin{cases} x(y-ax) & \text{for } y > ax, \\ 0 & \text{for } y < ax \end{cases}$
1.27	$\dfrac{q}{p^2q+a}$	$\sqrt{\pi}\,\dfrac{x^2}{4}\left(\dfrac{4}{ax^2y}\right)^{\frac{1}{2}} J_{\frac{1}{2},1}\left(3\sqrt[3]{\dfrac{ax^2y}{4}}\right) = \dfrac{x^2}{2!}\,{}_0F_2\left(\dfrac{3}{2}, 2; -\dfrac{ax^2y}{4}\right)$
1.28	$\dfrac{pq}{p^2q^2+a^2}$	$\dfrac{1}{a}\operatorname{bei}(2\sqrt{axy})$
1.29	$\dfrac{pq}{p^2q^2-a^2}$	$\dfrac{1}{2a}[I_0(2\sqrt{axy}) - J_0(2\sqrt{axy})]$
1.30	$\dfrac{pq}{(pq+b)^2+a^2}$	$\dfrac{\partial}{\partial x}\left[J_0(2\sqrt{bxy}) \overset{x}{*} \dfrac{1}{a}\operatorname{bei}(2\sqrt{axy})\right]$
1.31	$\dfrac{pq}{(pq+b)^2-a^2}$	$\dfrac{1}{2a}[J_0(2\sqrt{(b-a)xy}) - J_0(2\sqrt{(a+b)xy})]$

continued

№	$F(p, q)$	$f(x, y)$
1.32	$\dfrac{pq}{p^2q^2+apq+a^2}$	$\dfrac{2}{\sqrt{3a}}\dfrac{\partial}{\partial x}\left[J_0(\sqrt{2axy})\overset{x}{*}\operatorname{bei}\left(\sqrt{2\sqrt{3}axy}\right)\right]$
1.33	$\dfrac{q}{p(pq+a)}$	$\dfrac{x}{ay}J_2(2\sqrt{axy})$
1.34	$\dfrac{pq}{p^3q+a}$	$\dfrac{x^2}{2}\,{}_0F_3\left(1, \dfrac{4}{3}, \dfrac{5}{3}; -\dfrac{ax^3y}{27}\right)$
1.35	$\dfrac{pq}{p^3q+ap^2+b}$	$\dfrac{\partial}{\partial x}\left[J_0(2\sqrt{axy})\overset{x}{*}\dfrac{x^2}{2}\times {}_0F_3\left(1, \dfrac{4}{3}, \dfrac{5}{3}; -\dfrac{bx^3y}{27}\right)\right]$
1.36	$\dfrac{pq}{(p^2+a)(q^2+b)+cpq}$	$\int_0^x\int_0^y J_0(2\sqrt{a\xi(x-\xi)})\times J_0(2\sqrt{b\eta(y-\eta)})\,J_0(2\sqrt{c\xi\eta})\,d\xi\,d\eta$
1.37	$\dfrac{pq}{(p^2+a)(pq+b)-c}$	$\int_0^x d\xi\int_0^\xi J_0\left(2\sqrt{\left(b-\dfrac{c}{a}\right)y(x-\xi)}\right)\times J_0(2\sqrt{a\tau(\xi-\tau)})\,J_0\left(2\sqrt{\dfrac{c}{a}y\tau}\right)d\tau$
1.38	$\dfrac{p}{q(p+q)^2}+\dfrac{2p}{(p+q)^3}$	$\begin{cases} xy & \text{for } y>x, \\ 0 & \text{for } y<x \end{cases}$
1.39	$\dfrac{p^2q}{(pq+a)(pq+b)}$	$\dfrac{\partial}{\partial x}\left[\sqrt{\dfrac{y}{(b-a)x}}J_1(2\sqrt{(b-a)xy})\overset{x}{*}J_0(2\sqrt{axy})\right]$

continued

№	$F(p, q)$	$f(x, y)$
1.40	$\dfrac{p^2 q}{(pq+b)^2+a^2}$	$J_0(2\sqrt{bxy}) \overset{y}{*} \left[\operatorname{ber}(2\sqrt{axy}) - \dfrac{b}{a}\operatorname{bei}(2\sqrt{axy})\right]$
1.41	$\dfrac{p^2 q}{(pq+b)^2-a^2}$	$\dfrac{1}{2a}\left[\sqrt{(a+b)\dfrac{y}{x}}\, J_1(2\sqrt{(a+b)xy}) - \sqrt{(b-a)\dfrac{y}{x}}\, J_1(2\sqrt{(b-a)xy})\right]$
1.42	$\dfrac{p^2 q}{(p^2+a)(q^2+b)+cpq}$	$\int\limits_0^y J_0(2\sqrt{b\eta(y-\eta)})\, J_0(2\sqrt{cx\eta})\, d\eta - \int\limits_0^x \int\limits_0^y \sqrt{\dfrac{a\xi}{x-\xi}}\, J_1(2\sqrt{a\xi(x-\xi)}) \times J_0(2\sqrt{b\eta(y-\eta)})\, J_0(2\sqrt{c\xi\eta})\, d\xi\, d\eta$
1.43	$\dfrac{p^2 q}{p^2 q^2 + apq + a^2}$	$J_0(\sqrt{2axy}) \overset{y}{*} \left[\operatorname{ber}\left(\sqrt{2\sqrt{3}\, axy}\right) - \dfrac{1}{\sqrt{3}}\operatorname{bei}\left(\sqrt{2\sqrt{3}\, axy}\right)\right]$
1.44	$\dfrac{p^2 q}{p^2 q^2 + a^2}$	$\dfrac{1}{a}\dfrac{\partial}{\partial x}\operatorname{bei}(2\sqrt{axy}) = \sqrt{\dfrac{y}{2ax}}\,[\operatorname{bei}_1(2\sqrt{axy}) - \operatorname{ber}_1(2\sqrt{axy})]$
1.45	$\dfrac{p^2 q}{p^2 q^2 - a^2}$	$\dfrac{1}{2}\sqrt{\dfrac{y}{ax}}\,[J_1(2\sqrt{axy}) + I_1(2\sqrt{axy})]$

continued

№	$F(p, q)$	$f(x, y)$
1.46	$\frac{p^2q}{p^3q+a}$	$x\,{}_0F_3\left(\frac{2}{3}, 1, \frac{4}{3}; -\frac{ax^3y}{27}\right)$
1.47	$\frac{p^2q}{p^3q+ap^2+b}$	$\frac{\partial}{\partial x}\left[J_0(2\sqrt{axy}) \overset{x}{*} x \times {}_0F_3\left(\frac{2}{3}, 1, \frac{4}{3}; -\frac{bx^3y}{27}\right)\right]$
1.48	$\frac{pq(p+q)}{(p^2+1)(q^2+1)}$	$\sin(x+y)$
1.49	$\frac{pq(p+q)}{(p^2-1)(q^2-1)}$	$\operatorname{sh}(x+y)$
1.50	$\frac{p+q}{pq+a}$	$\frac{x+y}{\sqrt{axy}} J_1(2\sqrt{axy})$
1.51	$\frac{p^2q^2}{p^2q^2+a^2}$	$\operatorname{ber}(2\sqrt{axy})$
1.52	$\frac{p^2q^2}{p^2q^2-a^2}$	$\frac{1}{2}[J_0(2\sqrt{axy})+I_0(2\sqrt{axy})]$
1.53	$\frac{p^2q^2}{(pq+b)^2+a^2}$	$\frac{\partial}{\partial x}\left[J_0(2\sqrt{bxy}) \overset{x}{*}\left(\operatorname{ber}(2\sqrt{axy}) - \frac{b}{a}\operatorname{bei}(2\sqrt{axy})\right)\right]$
1.54	$\frac{p^2q^2}{p^2q^2+apq+a^2}$	$\frac{\partial}{\partial x}\left[J_0(\sqrt{2axy}) \overset{x}{*}\left(\operatorname{ber}\left(\sqrt{\sqrt{3}axy}\right) - \frac{1}{\sqrt{3}}\operatorname{bei}\left(\sqrt{2\sqrt{3}axy}\right)\right)\right]$

continued

№	$F(p, q)$	$f(x, y)$
1.55	$\dfrac{p^2q^2}{(p^2+a)(q^2+b)+cpq}$	$J_0(2\sqrt{cxy}) - \int_0^x \sqrt{\dfrac{a\xi}{x-\xi}}\, J_1(2\sqrt{a\xi(x-\xi)}) \times J_0(2\sqrt{cy\xi})\, d\xi - \int_0^y \sqrt{\dfrac{b\eta}{y-\eta}} \times J_1(2\sqrt{b\eta(y-\eta)})\, J_0(2\sqrt{cx\eta})\, d\eta + \int_0^x \int_0^y \sqrt{\dfrac{ab\xi\eta}{(x-\xi)(y-\eta)}} \times J_1(2\sqrt{a\xi(x-\xi)}) \times J_1(2\sqrt{b\eta(y-\eta)})\, J_0(2\sqrt{c\xi\eta})\, d\xi\, d\eta$
1.56	$\dfrac{p^3q}{p^3q+a}$	${}_0F_3\left(\dfrac{1}{3}, \dfrac{2}{3}, 1; -\dfrac{ax^3y}{27}\right)$
1.57	$\dfrac{p^3q}{p^3q+ap^2+b}$	$\dfrac{\partial}{\partial x}\left[J_0(2\sqrt{axy}) \overset{x}{*} {}_0F_3\left(\dfrac{1}{3}, \dfrac{2}{3}, 1; -\dfrac{bx^3y}{27}\right)\right]$
1.58	$\dfrac{pq(pq-1)}{(p^2+1)(q^2+1)}$	$\cos(x+y)$
1.59	$\dfrac{pq(pq+1)}{(p^2-1)(q^2-1)}$	$\operatorname{ch}(x+y)$
1.60	$\dfrac{pq(pq+b)}{(pq+b)^2+a^2}$	$\dfrac{\partial}{\partial x}\left[J_0(2\sqrt{bxy}) \overset{x}{*} \operatorname{ber}(2\sqrt{axy})\right]$

continued

№	$F(p, q)$	$f(x, y)$
1.61	$\dfrac{pq(pq+b)}{(pq+b)^2-a^2}$	$\frac{1}{2}[J_0(2\sqrt{(a+b)xy}) + J_0(2\sqrt{(b-a)xy})]$
1.62	$\dfrac{pq(pq+a)}{p^2q^2+apq+a^2}$	$\frac{\partial}{\partial x}\left\{J_0(\sqrt{2axy}) \overset{x}{*} \left[\operatorname{ber}\left(\sqrt{2\sqrt{3}axy}\right) + \frac{1}{\sqrt{3}}\operatorname{bei}\left(\sqrt{2\sqrt{3}axy}\right)\right]\right\}$
1.63	$\dfrac{(p+q)^2-bp-aq}{(p+q-a)(p+q-b)}$	$\begin{cases} e^{ax} & \text{for } y > x, \\ e^{by} & \text{for } y < x \end{cases}$
1.64	$\dfrac{pq(pq-a)}{p^2q^2+apq+a^2}$	$\frac{\partial}{\partial x}\left\{J_0(\sqrt{2axy}) \overset{x}{*} \left[\operatorname{ber}\left(\sqrt{2\sqrt{3}axy}\right) - \sqrt{3}\operatorname{bei}\left(\sqrt{2\sqrt{3}axy}\right)\right]\right\}$
1.65	$\dfrac{pq[(p+q)^2-(2a+b)p-(2b+a)q+a^2+b^2]}{(p-a)(q-b)\times(p+q-a)(p+q-b)}$	$\begin{cases} e^{by} & \text{for } y > x, \\ e^{ax} & \text{for } y < x \end{cases}$
1.66	$\dfrac{1}{pq(p+q)}$	$\frac{1}{2}\begin{cases} x^2y - \frac{x^3}{3} & \text{for } y > x, \\ xy^2 - \frac{y^3}{3} & \text{for } y < x \end{cases}$
1.67	$\dfrac{q}{p^2q^2+a^2}$	$-\frac{1}{a^2}\frac{\partial}{\partial y}\operatorname{ber}(2\sqrt{axy}) = -\frac{1}{a}\sqrt{\frac{x}{2ay}}[\operatorname{ber}_1(2\sqrt{axy}) + \operatorname{bei}_1(2\sqrt{axy})]$

continued

№	$F(p, q)$	$f(x, y)$
1.68	$\dfrac{q}{(p^2q^2 - a^2)}$	$\dfrac{1}{2a}\sqrt{\dfrac{x}{ay}}\,[I_1(2\sqrt{axy}) - J_1(2\sqrt{axy})]$
1.69	$\dfrac{q}{(pq+b)^2 + a^2}$	$\dfrac{1}{a} J_0(2\sqrt{bxy}) \overset{x}{*} \operatorname{bei}(2\sqrt{axy})$
1.70	$\dfrac{pq}{p^3q^2 + a}$	$\dfrac{x^2y}{2}\, {}_0F_4\left(\dfrac{3}{2}, 1, \dfrac{4}{3}, \dfrac{5}{3}; -\dfrac{ax^3y^2}{3^3 2^2}\right)$
1.71	$\dfrac{pq}{p^4q + a}$	$\dfrac{x^3}{3!}\, {}_0F_4\left(1, \dfrac{5}{4}, \dfrac{6}{4}, \dfrac{7}{4}; -\dfrac{ax^4y}{64}\right)$
1.72	$\dfrac{q}{p^3q + a}$	$\dfrac{x^3}{3!}\, {}_0F_3\left(\dfrac{4}{3}, \dfrac{5}{3}, 2; -\dfrac{ax^3y}{27}\right)$
1.73	$\dfrac{p^2}{p^2q^2 - a^2}$	$\dfrac{y}{2ax}[J_2(2\sqrt{axy}) + I_2(2\sqrt{axy})]$
1.74	$\dfrac{p^2}{p^2q^2 + a^2}$	$\dfrac{y}{ax}\Big\{\operatorname{bei}(2\sqrt{axy}) + \dfrac{1}{\sqrt{2axy}}[\operatorname{ber}_1(2\sqrt{axy}) + \operatorname{bei}_1(2\sqrt{axy})]\Big\} = -\dfrac{y}{ax}\operatorname{bei}_2(2\sqrt{axy})$
1.75	$\dfrac{q}{p(p^2q + a)}$	$\sqrt{\pi}\,\dfrac{x^3}{2^3}\left(\dfrac{4}{ax^2y}\right)^{5/6} J_{1,3/2}\left(3\sqrt[3]{\dfrac{ax^2y}{4}}\right) = \dfrac{x^3}{3!}\, {}_0F_2\left(2, \dfrac{5}{2}; -\dfrac{ax^2y}{4}\right)$
1.76	$\dfrac{p^2q}{p^3q^2 + a}$	$xy\, {}_0F_4\left(\dfrac{3}{2}, \dfrac{2}{3}, 1, \dfrac{4}{3}; -\dfrac{ax^3y^2}{3^3 2^2}\right)$

continued

№	$F(p, q)$	$f(x, y)$
1.77	$\dfrac{p^2q}{p^4q+a}$	$\dfrac{x^2}{2!}\,{}_0F_4\left(\dfrac{3}{4}, 1, \dfrac{5}{4}, \dfrac{6}{4}; -\dfrac{ax^4y}{4^4}\right)$
1.78	$\dfrac{pq^2}{p^3q^2+a}$	$\dfrac{x^2}{2!}\,{}_0F_4\left(\dfrac{1}{2}, 1, \dfrac{4}{3}, \dfrac{5}{3}; -\dfrac{ax^3y^2}{3^32^2}\right)$
1.79	$\dfrac{p^2q^2}{p^3q^2+a}$	$x\cdot{}_0F_4\left(\dfrac{1}{2}, \dfrac{2}{3}, 1, \dfrac{4}{3}; -\dfrac{ax^3y^2}{3^32^2}\right)$
1.80	$\dfrac{p^3q}{p^3q^2+a}$	$y\,{}_0F_4\left(\dfrac{3}{2}, \dfrac{1}{3}, \dfrac{2}{3}, 1; -\dfrac{ax^3y^2}{3^32^2}\right)$
1.81	$\dfrac{p^3q}{p^4q+a}$	$x\,{}_0F_4\left(\dfrac{2}{4}, \dfrac{3}{4}, 1, \dfrac{5}{4}; -\dfrac{ax^4y}{4^4}\right)$
1.82	$\dfrac{q(pq+a)}{(p^2q^2+a^2)}$	$-\sqrt{\dfrac{2x}{ay}}\,\mathrm{ber}_1(2\sqrt{axy})$
1.83	$\dfrac{q(pq-a)}{p^2q^2+a^2}$	$\sqrt{\dfrac{2x}{ay}}\,\mathrm{bei}_1(2\sqrt{axy})$
1.84	$\dfrac{p(pq-a)}{p^2q^2+apq+a^2}$	$J_0(2\sqrt{axy})\overset{y}{*}\left[\mathrm{ber}\left(\sqrt{2\sqrt{3}axy}\right)-\sqrt{3}\,\mathrm{bei}\left(\sqrt{2\sqrt{3}axy}\right)\right]$
1.85	$\dfrac{q(pq+b)}{(pq+b)^2+a^2}$	$J_0(2\sqrt{bxy})\overset{x}{*}\mathrm{ber}(2\sqrt{axy})$
1.86	$\dfrac{p(bpq+b^2-a^2)}{(pq+b)^2-a^2}$	$\dfrac{1}{2}\left[\sqrt{(b+a)\dfrac{y}{x}}\,J_1\left(2\sqrt{(b+a)\dfrac{y}{x}}\right)+\sqrt{(b-a)\dfrac{y}{x}}\,J_1\left(2\sqrt{(b-a)\dfrac{y}{x}}\right)\right]$
1.87	$\dfrac{p(ap^2+b)}{p^3q+ap^2+b}$	$-\dfrac{\partial^2}{\partial x^2}\left[J_0(2\sqrt{axy})\overset{x}{*}{}_0F_3\left(\dfrac{1}{3}, \dfrac{2}{3}, 1; -\dfrac{bx^3y}{27}\right)\right]$

continued

№	$F(p, q)$	$f(x, y)$
1.88	$\frac{p^3q^2}{p^3q^2+a}$	${}_0F_4\left(\frac{1}{2}, \frac{1}{3}, \frac{2}{3}, 1; -\frac{ax^3y^2}{3^32^2}\right)$
1.89	$\frac{p^4q}{p^4q+a}$	${}_0F_4\left(\frac{1}{4}, \frac{2}{4}, \frac{3}{4}, 1; -\frac{ax^4y}{4^4}\right)$
1.90	$\frac{pq}{p^3q^3+a^3}$	$\frac{1}{3a^2}\left[J_0(2\sqrt{axy}) - \frac{\partial}{\partial x}\left\{I_0(\sqrt{2axy}) \overset{x}{*} \left(\operatorname{ber}\left(\sqrt{2\sqrt{3}axy}\right) - \sqrt{3}\operatorname{bei}\left(\sqrt{2\sqrt{3}axy}\right)\right)\right\}\right]$
1.91	$\frac{pq}{p^3q^3+ap^2q^2+a^2pq+a^3}$	$\frac{1}{2a^2}\left[J_0(2\sqrt{axy}) - \operatorname{ber}(2\sqrt{axy}) + \operatorname{bei}(2\sqrt{axy})\right]$
1.92	$\frac{p}{q(p^2q^2+a^2)}$	$\frac{\sqrt{y}}{a^2x}\left[\frac{1}{\sqrt{2ax}}\operatorname{bei}_1(2\sqrt{axy}) - \frac{1}{\sqrt{2ax}}\operatorname{ber}_1(2\sqrt{axy}) - \sqrt{y}\operatorname{ber}_0(2\sqrt{axy})\right] = \frac{y}{a^2x}\operatorname{ber}_2(2\sqrt{axy})$
1.93	$\frac{p}{q(p^2q^2-a^2)}$	$\frac{y}{2a^2x}\left[I_2(2\sqrt{axy}) - J_2(2\sqrt{axy})\right]$
1.94	$\frac{q}{p(p^3q+a)}$	$\frac{x^4}{4!}\,{}_0F_3\left(\frac{5}{3}, \frac{6}{3}, \frac{7}{3}; -\frac{ax^3y}{27}\right)$

continued

№	$F(p, q)$	$f(x, y)$
1.95	$\dfrac{p^2q}{p^3q^3+a^3}$	$\dfrac{1}{3a}\Big\{I_0(\sqrt{2axy}) \overset{y}{*} \Big[\operatorname{ber}\big(\sqrt{2\sqrt{3}axy}\big)+ + \sqrt{3}\operatorname{bei}\big(\sqrt{2\sqrt{3}axy}\big)\Big] - -\sqrt{\dfrac{y}{ax}}J_1(2\sqrt{axy})\Big\}$
1.96	$\dfrac{p^2q}{p^3q^3+ap^2q^2+a^2pq+a^3}$	$-\dfrac{1}{2a}\sqrt{\dfrac{y}{ax}}\,[J_1(2\sqrt{axy})+ + \sqrt{2}\operatorname{ber}_1(2\sqrt{axy})]$
1.97	$\dfrac{p^2q}{p^3q^3-ap^2q^2+a^2pq-a^3}$	$\dfrac{1}{2a}\sqrt{\dfrac{y}{ax}}\,[I_1(2\sqrt{axy})- -\sqrt{2}\operatorname{bei}_1(2\sqrt{axy})]$
1.98	$\dfrac{p^2}{q(p^2q^2+a^2)}$	$\dfrac{1}{a^2x^2}\Big[2y\operatorname{ber}_0(2\sqrt{axy})+ +(2-axy)\sqrt{\dfrac{y}{2ax}}\operatorname{ber}_1(2\sqrt{axy})- -(2+axy)\sqrt{\dfrac{y}{2ax}}\operatorname{bei}_1(2\sqrt{axy})\Big]= =\dfrac{1}{\sqrt{2}}\left(\dfrac{y}{ax}\right)^{3/2}[\operatorname{ber}_3(2\sqrt{axy})+ +\operatorname{bei}_3(2\sqrt{axy})]$
1.99	$\dfrac{p^2}{q(p^2q^2-a^2)}$	$\dfrac{1}{2}\left(\dfrac{y}{ax}\right)^{3/2}[J_3(2\sqrt{axy})+ +I_3(2\sqrt{axy})]$

continued

№	$F(p, q)$	$f(x, y)$
1.100	$\frac{pq(pq-a)}{p^3q^3+a^3}$	$\frac{2}{3a}\left[\frac{\partial}{\partial x}\{I_0(\sqrt{2axy}) \overset{x}{*} \mathrm{ber}(\sqrt{2\sqrt{3}axy})\} - J_0'(2\sqrt{axy})\right]$
1.101	$\frac{p^2q^2}{p^3q^3+a^3}$	$\frac{1}{3a}\left\{\frac{\partial}{\partial x}\left[I_0(\sqrt{2axy}) \overset{x}{*} (\mathrm{ber}(\sqrt{2\sqrt{3}axy}) + \sqrt{3}\,\mathrm{bei}(\sqrt{2\sqrt{3}axy}))\right] - J_0(2\sqrt{axy})\right\}$
1.102	$\frac{p^2q^2}{p^3q^3+ap^2q^2+a^2pq+a^3}$	$\frac{1}{2a}[-J_0(2\sqrt{axy}) + \mathrm{ber}(2\sqrt{axy}) + \mathrm{bei}(2\sqrt{axy})]$
1.103	$\frac{p^3q}{p^3q^3+a^3}$	$\frac{1}{3}\left[\frac{y}{ax}J_2(2\sqrt{axy}) + \left\{2\sqrt{\frac{2y}{ax}}I_1(\sqrt{2axy})\right\} \overset{y}{*} \mathrm{ber}(\sqrt{2\sqrt{3}axy})\right]$
1.104	$\frac{p^3q}{p^3q^3+ap^2q^2+a^2pq+a^3}$	$\frac{y}{2ax}\left[J_2(2\sqrt{axy}) + \sqrt{\frac{2}{axy}}\mathrm{ber}_1(2\sqrt{axy}) + \mathrm{ber}_0(2\sqrt{axy}) + \mathrm{bei}_0(2\sqrt{axy})\right] = \frac{y}{2ax}[J_2(2\sqrt{axy}) - \mathrm{ber}_2(2\sqrt{axy}) - \mathrm{bei}_2(2\sqrt{axy})]$

continued

№	$F(p, q)$	$f(x, y)$
1.105	$\frac{p^3q^2}{p^3q^3+a^3}$	$\frac{1}{3}\left[\sqrt{\frac{y}{ax}}J_1(2\sqrt{axy})+\right.$ $\left.+2I_0(\sqrt{2axy})\overset{y}{*}\operatorname{ber}\left(\sqrt{2\sqrt{3}axy}\right)\right]$
1.106	$\frac{p^3q^2}{p^3q^3+ap^2q^2+a^2pq+a^3}$	$\frac{1}{2}\sqrt{\frac{y}{ax}}[J_1(2\sqrt{axy})+$ $+\sqrt{2}\operatorname{bei}_1(2\sqrt{axy})]$
1.107	$\frac{p^2q(pq-2a)}{p^3q^3+a^3}$	$\sqrt{\frac{y}{ax}}J_0(2\sqrt{axy})-$ $-\frac{2}{\sqrt{3}}I_0(\sqrt{2axy})\overset{y}{*}\operatorname{bei}\left(\sqrt{2\sqrt{3}axy}\right)$
1.108	$\frac{pq(p^2q+q^2+p)}{(p^3-1)(q^3-1)}$	$\frac{1}{3}[e^{x+y}+\varepsilon e^{\varepsilon x+\varepsilon^2 y}+\varepsilon^2 e^{\varepsilon^2 x+\varepsilon y}]$, $\varepsilon=e^{\frac{2\pi i}{3}}$
1.109	$\frac{p^3q^3}{p^3q^3+a^3}$	$\frac{1}{3}\left[J_0(2\sqrt{axy})+2\frac{\partial}{\partial x}\times\right.$ $\left.\times\left\{I_0(\sqrt{2axy})\overset{x}{*}\operatorname{ber}\left(\sqrt{2\sqrt{3}axy}\right)\right\}\right]$
1.110	$\frac{p^3q^3}{p^3q^3+ap^2q^2+a^2pq+a^3}$	$\frac{1}{2}[J_0(2\sqrt{axy})+\operatorname{ber}(2\sqrt{axy})-$ $-\operatorname{bei}(2\sqrt{axy})]$
1.111	$\frac{pq(p^2q^2+2a^2)}{p^3q^3+a^3}$	$J_0(2\sqrt{axy})+\frac{2}{\sqrt{3}}\frac{\partial}{\partial x}\times$ $\times\left[I_0(\sqrt{2axy})\overset{x}{*}\operatorname{bei}\left(\sqrt{2\sqrt{3}xy}\right)\right]$

continued

№	$F(p, q)$	$f(x, y)$
1.112	$\dfrac{pq(p^2q^2+2a^2)}{p^3q^3-a^3}$	$I_0(2\sqrt{axy})-\dfrac{2}{\sqrt{3}}\dfrac{\partial}{\partial x}\times$ $\times[J_0(\sqrt{2axy})\overset{x}{*}\operatorname{bei}(\sqrt{2\sqrt{3}axy})]$
1.113	$\dfrac{p^2q^2(pq-2a)}{p^3q^3+a^3}$	$J_0(2\sqrt{axy})-\dfrac{2}{\sqrt{3}}\dfrac{\partial}{\partial x}\times$ $\times[I_0(\sqrt{2axy})\overset{x}{*}\operatorname{bei}(\sqrt{2\sqrt{3}axy})]$
1.114	$\dfrac{pq(p^2q^2+pq+1)}{(p^3-1)(q^3-1)}$	$\dfrac{1}{3}[e^{x+y}+e^{\varepsilon x+\varepsilon^2 y}+e^{\varepsilon^2 x+\varepsilon y}]$, $\varepsilon=e^{\frac{2\pi i}{3}}$
1.115	$\dfrac{pq(2p^2q^2-apq-a^2)}{p^3q^3-a^3}$	$2\dfrac{\partial}{\partial x}[J_0(\sqrt{2axy})\overset{x}{*}$ $\operatorname{ber}(\sqrt{2\sqrt{3}axy})]$
1.116	$\dfrac{pq(p^2q^2+apq-2a^2)}{p^3q^3-a^3}$	$\dfrac{\partial}{\partial x}[J_0(\sqrt{2axy})\overset{x}{*}$ $\{\operatorname{ber}(\sqrt{2\sqrt{3}axy})+$ $+\sqrt{3}\operatorname{bei}(\sqrt{2\sqrt{3}axy})\}]$
1.117	$\dfrac{1}{p^2q^2(p+q)}$	$\dfrac{1}{12}\begin{cases} x^3y^2-\dfrac{x^4y}{2}+\dfrac{x^5}{10} & \text{for } y>x, \\ x^2y^3-\dfrac{xy^4}{2}+\dfrac{y^5}{10} & \text{for } y<x \end{cases}$
1.118	$\dfrac{q}{p^2(p^3q+a)}$	$\dfrac{x^5}{5!}\cdot {}_0F_3\left(2, \dfrac{7}{3}, \dfrac{8}{3}; -\dfrac{ax^3y}{27}\right)$
1.119	$\dfrac{q(2p^2q^2-apq-a^2)}{p^3q^3-a^3}$	$2J_0(\sqrt{2axy})\overset{x}{*}\operatorname{ber}(\sqrt{2\sqrt{3}axy})$

continued

№	$F(p, q)$	$f(x, y)$
1.120	$\frac{pq}{p^4q^4 + a^4}$	$\frac{1}{2\sqrt{2}\pi a^3} \times$ $\times \Big[\frac{\operatorname{sh}\sqrt{\sqrt{2}axy} \cdot \sin\sqrt{\sqrt{2}axy}}{\sqrt{x}}$ $\overset{x}{*} \frac{\operatorname{ch}\sqrt{\sqrt{2}axy} + \cos\sqrt{2\sqrt{2}axy}}{\sqrt{x}} -$ $- \frac{\operatorname{ch}\sqrt{\sqrt{2}axy} \cdot \cos\sqrt{\sqrt{2}axy}}{\sqrt{x}}$ $\overset{x}{*} \frac{\operatorname{ch}\sqrt{2\sqrt{2}axy} - \cos\sqrt{2\sqrt{2}axy}}{\sqrt{x}} \Big]$
1.121	$\frac{pq}{p^4q^4 - a^2}$	$\frac{1}{4a^3}[I_0(2\sqrt{axy}) - J_0(2\sqrt{axy}) -$ $- 2\operatorname{bei}(2\sqrt{axy})]$
1.122	$\frac{p^2q}{p^4q^4 + a^4}$	$\frac{1}{2a^2}\operatorname{bei}\left(\sqrt{2\sqrt{2}axy}\right) \overset{y}{*}$ $\left[I_0\left(\sqrt{2\sqrt{2}axy}\right) -\right.$ $\left.- J_0\left(\sqrt{2\sqrt{2}axy}\right)\right]$
1.123	$\frac{p^2q}{p^4q^4 - a^4}$	$\frac{1}{4a^2}\sqrt{\frac{y}{ax}}[J_1(2\sqrt{axy}) +$ $+ I_1(2\sqrt{axy}) + \sqrt{2}\{\operatorname{ber}_1(2\sqrt{axy}) -$ $- \operatorname{bei}_1(2\sqrt{axy})\}]$
1.124	$\frac{p^2q^2}{p^4q^4 + a^4}$	$\frac{1}{2\pi a^2} \frac{\operatorname{sh}\sqrt{\sqrt{2}axy}\,\sin\sqrt{\sqrt{2}axy}}{\sqrt{x}}$ $\overset{x}{*} \frac{\operatorname{ch}\sqrt{2\sqrt{2}axy} - \cos\sqrt{2\sqrt{2}axy}}{\sqrt{x}}$

continued

№	$F(p, q)$	$f(x, y)$
1.125	$\frac{p^2q^2}{p^4q^4-a^4}$	$\frac{1}{4a^2}[J_0(2\sqrt{axy})+I_0(2\sqrt{axy})-2\,\mathrm{ber}(2\sqrt{axy})]$
1.126	$\frac{p^2q^2}{(p^2q^2-a^2)^2}$	$\frac{1}{4a}\sqrt{\frac{xy}{a}}[I_1(2\sqrt{axy})-J_1(2\sqrt{axy})]$
1.127	$\frac{p^3q}{p^4q^4+a^2}$	$\frac{1}{2\sqrt{2}a}\Big[\mathrm{ber}\big(\sqrt{2\sqrt{2}axy}\big)\overset{y}{*}\sqrt{\frac{\sqrt{2}y}{ax}}\Big\{I_1\big(\sqrt{2\sqrt{2}axy}\big)-J_1\big(\sqrt{2\sqrt{2}axy}\big)\Big\}+\mathrm{bei}\big(\sqrt{2\sqrt{2}axy}\big)\overset{y}{*}\sqrt{\frac{\sqrt{2}y}{ax}}\Big\{I_1\big(\sqrt{2\sqrt{2}axy}\big)+J_1\big(\sqrt{2\sqrt{2}axy}\big)\Big\}\Big]$
1.128	$\frac{p^3q}{p^4q^4-a^4}$	$\frac{y}{4a^2x}[I_2(2\sqrt{axy})-J_2(2\sqrt{axy})+2\,\mathrm{ber}_2(2\sqrt{axy})]$
1.129	$\frac{p^3q^2}{p^4q^4+a^4}$	$\frac{1}{2\sqrt{2}a}\Big[\mathrm{ber}\big(\sqrt{2\sqrt{2}axy}\big)\overset{y}{*}\Big\{I_0\big(\sqrt{2\sqrt{2}axy}\big)-J_0\big(\sqrt{2\sqrt{2}axy}\big)\Big\}+\mathrm{bei}\big(\sqrt{2\sqrt{2}axy}\big)\overset{y}{*}\Big\{I_0\big(\sqrt{2\sqrt{2}axy}\big)+J_0\big(\sqrt{2\sqrt{2}axy}\big)\Big\}\Big]$
1.130	$\frac{p^3q^2}{p^4q^4-a^4}$	$\frac{1}{4a}\sqrt{\frac{y}{ax}}[I_1(2\sqrt{axy})-J_1(2\sqrt{axy})-\sqrt{2}\{\mathrm{ber}_1(2\sqrt{axy})+\mathrm{bei}_1(2\sqrt{axy})\}]$

continued

№	$F(p, q)$	$f(x, y)$
1.131	$\dfrac{p^4q}{p^4q^4+a^4}$	$\dfrac{1}{\sqrt{2a}} \operatorname{ber}\left(\sqrt{2\sqrt{2axy}}\right) \overset{y}{*} \dfrac{y}{x}\left[J_2\left(\sqrt{2\sqrt{2axy}}\right)+I_2\left(\sqrt{2\sqrt{2axy}}\right)\right]$
1.132	$\dfrac{p^4q}{p^4q^4-a^4}$	$\dfrac{1}{4}\left(\dfrac{y}{ax}\right)^{3/2}\left[J_3(2\sqrt{axy}) + I_3(2\sqrt{axy}) + \sqrt{2}\operatorname{ber}_3(2\sqrt{axy}) + \sqrt{2}\operatorname{bei}_3(2\sqrt{axy})\right]$
1.133	$\dfrac{p^3q^3}{p^4q^4+a^4}$	$\dfrac{1}{2\sqrt{2a\pi}} \times \left[\dfrac{\operatorname{ch}\sqrt{\sqrt{2axy}}\cos\sqrt{2\sqrt{2axy}}}{\sqrt{x}} \overset{x}{*} \dfrac{\operatorname{ch}\sqrt{2\sqrt{2axy}}-\cos\sqrt{2\sqrt{2axy}}}{\sqrt{x}} + \dfrac{\operatorname{sh}\sqrt{\sqrt{2axy}}\cdot\sin\sqrt{\sqrt{2axy}}}{\sqrt{x}} \overset{x}{*} \dfrac{\operatorname{ch}\sqrt{2\sqrt{2axy}}+\cos\sqrt{2\sqrt{2axy}}}{\sqrt{x}}\right]$
1.134	$\dfrac{p^3q^3}{p^4q^4-a^4}$	$\dfrac{1}{4a}\left[I_0(2\sqrt{axy}) - J_0(2\sqrt{axy}) + 2\operatorname{bei}(2\sqrt{axy})\right]$
1.135	$\dfrac{p^4q^2}{p^4q^4+a^4}$	$\dfrac{1}{2}\operatorname{ber}\left(\sqrt{2\sqrt{2axy}}\right) \overset{y}{*} \sqrt{\dfrac{\sqrt{2y}}{ax}}\left[J_1\left(\sqrt{2\sqrt{2axy}}\right) + I_1\left(\sqrt{2\sqrt{2axy}}\right)\right]$

continued

№	$F(p, q)$	$f(x, y)$
1.136	$\dfrac{p^4q^2}{p^4q^4-a^4}$	$\dfrac{y}{4ax}\left[J_2(2\sqrt{axy})+I_2(2\sqrt{axy})-2\,\mathrm{bei}_2(2\sqrt{axy})\right]$
1.137	$\dfrac{pq(p^2q^2+a^2)}{p^4q^4+a^4}$	$\dfrac{1}{\sqrt{2a\pi}}\,\dfrac{\mathrm{sh}\sqrt{\sqrt{2}\,axy}\,\sin\sqrt{\sqrt{2}\,axy}}{\sqrt{x}}\overset{x}{*}\dfrac{\mathrm{ch}\sqrt{2\sqrt{2}\,axy}+\cos\sqrt{2\sqrt{2}\,axy}}{\sqrt{x}}$
1.138	$\dfrac{pq(p^2q^2-a^2)}{p^4q^4+a^4}$	$\dfrac{1}{\sqrt{2a\pi}}\,\dfrac{\mathrm{ch}\sqrt{\sqrt{2}\,axy}\,\cos\sqrt{\sqrt{2}\,axy}}{\sqrt{x}}\overset{x}{*}\dfrac{\mathrm{ch}\sqrt{2\sqrt{2}\,axy}-\cos\sqrt{2\sqrt{2}\,axy}}{\sqrt{x}}$
1.139	$\dfrac{pq(p^2q^2+a^2)}{(p^2q^2-a^2)^2}$	$\dfrac{1}{2}\sqrt{\dfrac{xy}{a}}\left[J_1(2\sqrt{axy})+I_1(2\sqrt{axy})\right]$
1.140	$\dfrac{q(2p^2q^2-apq-a^2)}{p(p^3q^3-a^3)}$	$\left\{2\sqrt{\dfrac{2x}{ay}}\,J_1(\sqrt{2axy})\right\}\overset{x}{*}\mathrm{ber}\left(\sqrt{2\sqrt{3}\,axy}\right)$
1.141	$\dfrac{p^4q^3}{p^4q^4+a^4}$	$\dfrac{1}{2}\,\mathrm{ber}\left(\sqrt{2\sqrt{2}\,axy}\right)\overset{y}{*}\left[J_0\left(\sqrt{2\sqrt{2}\,axy}\right)+I_0\left(\sqrt{2\sqrt{2}\,axy}\right)\right]$
1.142	$\dfrac{p^4q^3}{p^4q^4-a^4}$	$\dfrac{1}{4}\sqrt{\dfrac{y}{ax}}\left[J_1(2\sqrt{axy})+I_1(2\sqrt{axy})-\sqrt{2}\left\{\mathrm{ber}_1(2\sqrt{axy})-\mathrm{bei}_1(2\sqrt{axy})\right\}\right]$

continued

№	$F(p, q)$	$f(x, y)$
1.143	$\frac{p^4q^4}{p^4q^4 + a^4}$	$\frac{1}{2\pi}\frac{\operatorname{ch}\sqrt{\sqrt{2}\,axy}\cdot\cos\sqrt{\sqrt{2}\,axy}}{\sqrt{x}} \overset{x}{*} \frac{\operatorname{ch}\sqrt{2\sqrt{2}\,axy}+\cos\sqrt{2\sqrt{2}\,axy}}{\sqrt{x}}$
1.144	$\frac{p^4q^4}{p^4q^4 - a^4}$	$\frac{1}{4}[J_0(2\sqrt{axy}) + I_0(2\sqrt{axy}) + 2\operatorname{ber}(2\sqrt{axy})]$
1.145	$\left(1 - \frac{1}{p} - \frac{1}{q}\right)^{-1}$	$e^{x+y}J_0(2i\sqrt{xy})$
1.146	$\frac{pq}{p^nq + a}$ $n > 0$	$\frac{x^{n-1}}{(n-1)!}\,{}_0F_n\left(1,\ 1+\frac{1}{n},\ 1+\frac{2}{n},\ \ldots,\ 1+\frac{n-1}{n};\ -\frac{ax^ny}{n^n}\right)$
1.147	$\frac{pq}{(pq+1)^{n+1}}$	$\frac{(xy)^{\frac{n}{2}}}{\Gamma(n+1)}J_n(2\sqrt{xy})$
1.148	$\frac{m!}{p^mq^n}\cdot\frac{q^{m+1} - p^{m+1}}{q - p}$	$(x+y)^m$
1.149	$\frac{p^nq}{p^nq + n}$ $n > 0$	${}_0F_n\left(\frac{1}{n},\ \frac{2}{n},\ \ldots,\ \frac{n-1}{n},\ 1;\ -\frac{ax^ny}{n^n}\right)$
1.150	$\frac{p^{n-m+1}q}{p^nq + a}$ $m,\ n > 0$	$\frac{x^{m-1}}{(m-1)!}\,{}_0F_n\left(\frac{m}{n},\ \frac{m+1}{n},\ \ldots,\ \frac{m+n-1}{n};\ -\frac{ax^ny}{n^n}\right)$
1.151	$\frac{q}{p^{n-3}(p^3q + a)}$	$\frac{x^n}{n!}\,{}_0F_3\left(\frac{n+1}{n},\ \frac{n+2}{n}.\ \frac{n+3}{a};\ -\frac{ax^3y}{27}\right)$

continued

№	$F(p, q)$	$f(x, y)$
1.152	$\frac{q}{p^{n-1}(p^2q+a)}$	$\sqrt{\pi}\,\frac{x^{n+1}}{2^{n+1}}\left(\frac{4}{ax^2y}\right)^{\frac{2n+1}{6}}\times$ $\times J_{\frac{n}{2},\,\frac{n+1}{2}}\left(3\sqrt[3]{\frac{ax^2y}{4}}\right)=$ $=\frac{x^{n+1}}{(n+1)!}\,{}_0F_2\left(\frac{n+2}{2}, \frac{n+3}{2}; -\frac{ax^2y}{4}\right)$
1.153	$\frac{q}{p^{4n-1}(p^2q^2+a^2)}$	$\frac{(-1)^n}{a}\left(\frac{x}{ay}\right)^{2n}\operatorname{bei}_{4n}(2\sqrt{axy})$
1.154	$\frac{q^2}{p^{4n-2}(p^2q^2+a^2)}$	$(-1)^n\left(\frac{x}{ay}\right)^{2n}\operatorname{ber}_{4n}(2\sqrt{axy})$
1.155	$\frac{q}{p^{4n}(p^2q^2+a^2)}$	$\frac{(-1)^{n+1}}{a\sqrt{2}}\left(\frac{x}{ay}\right)^{2n+\frac{1}{2}}\times$ $\times[\operatorname{ber}_{4n+1}(2\sqrt{axy})+\operatorname{bei}_{4n+1}(2\sqrt{axy})]$
1.156	$\frac{q^2}{p^{4n-1}(p^2q^2+a^2)}$	$\frac{(-1)^{n+1}}{\sqrt{2}}\left(\frac{x}{ay}\right)^{2n+\frac{1}{2}}\times$ $\times[\operatorname{ber}_{4n+1}(2\sqrt{axy})-\operatorname{bei}_{4n+1}(2\sqrt{axy})]$
1.157	$\frac{q(pq+a)}{p^{4n}(p^2q^2+a^2)}$	$(-1)^{n+1}\sqrt{2}\left(\frac{x}{ay}\right)^{2n+\frac{1}{2}}\times$ $\times\operatorname{ber}_{4n+1}(2\sqrt{axy})$
1.158	$\frac{q(pq-a)}{p^{4n}(p^2q^2+a^2)}$	$(-1)^n\sqrt{2}\left(\frac{x}{ay}\right)^{2n+\frac{1}{2}}\operatorname{bei}_{4n+1}(2\sqrt{axy})$
1.159	$\frac{q}{p^{4n+1}(p^2q^2+a^2)}$	$\frac{(-1)^n}{a}\left(\frac{x}{ay}\right)^{2n+1}\operatorname{ber}_{4n+2}(2\sqrt{axy})$

continued

№	$F(p, q)$	$f(x, y)$
1.160	$\dfrac{q^2}{p^{4n}(p^2q^2+a^2)}$	$(-1)^{n+1}\left(\dfrac{x}{ay}\right)^{2n+1}\mathrm{bei}_{4n+2}(2\sqrt{axy})$
1.161	$\dfrac{q}{p^{4n+2}(p^2q^2+a^2)}$	$\dfrac{(-1)^{n+1}}{a\sqrt{2}}\left(\dfrac{x}{ay}\right)^{2n+\frac{3}{2}}[\mathrm{ber}_{4n+3}(2\sqrt{axy})-$ $-\mathrm{bei}_{4n+3}(2\sqrt{axy})]$
1.162	$\dfrac{q^2}{p^{4n+1}(p^2q^2+a^2)}$	$\dfrac{(-1)^n}{\sqrt{2}}\left(\dfrac{x}{ay}\right)^{2n+\frac{3}{2}}[\mathrm{ber}_{4n+3}(2\sqrt{axy})+$ $+\mathrm{bei}_{4n+3}(2\sqrt{axy})]$
1.163	$\dfrac{q(pq+a)}{p^{4n+2}(p^2q^2+a^2)}$	$(-1)^n\sqrt{2}\left(\dfrac{x}{ay}\right)^{2n+\frac{3}{2}}\mathrm{bei}_{4n+3}(2\sqrt{axy})$
1.164	$\dfrac{q(pq-a)}{p^{4n+2}(p^2q^2+a^2)}$	$(-1)^n\sqrt{2}\left(\dfrac{x}{ay}\right)^{2n+\frac{3}{2}}\mathrm{ber}_{4n+3}(2\sqrt{axy})$
1.165	$\dfrac{pq}{(pq)^n+a^n}$	$\dfrac{1}{na^{n-1}}\sum\limits_{k=0}^{n-1}\dfrac{I_0\left(2\varepsilon^{k+\frac{1}{2}}\sqrt{axy}\right)}{\varepsilon^{(n-1)(2k+1)}}, \quad \varepsilon=e^{\frac{\pi i}{n}}$
1.166	$\dfrac{(pq)^{n-m+1}}{(pq)^n+a^n}$ $0<m\leqslant n$	$\dfrac{1}{na^{m-1}}\sum\limits_{k=0}^{n-1}\dfrac{I_0\left(2\varepsilon^{k+\frac{1}{2}}\sqrt{axy}\right)}{\varepsilon^{(m-1)(2k+1)}}; \quad \varepsilon=e^{\frac{\pi i}{n}}$
1.167	$\dfrac{p^2q^2}{(pq)^n+a^n}$	$\dfrac{1}{na^{n-2}}\sum\limits_{k=0}^{n-1}\dfrac{I_0\left(2\varepsilon^{k+\frac{1}{2}}\sqrt{axy}\right)}{\varepsilon^{(n-2)(2k+1)}}; \quad \varepsilon=e^{\frac{\pi i}{n}}$
1.168	$\dfrac{(pq)^{n-m+1}}{(pq)^n-a^n}$ $0<m\leqslant n$	$\dfrac{1}{na^{m-1}}\sum\limits_{k=0}^{n-1}\dfrac{I_0\left(2\varepsilon^{\frac{k}{2}}\sqrt{axy}\right)}{\varepsilon^{(m-1)k}}; \quad \varepsilon=e^{\frac{2\pi i}{n}}$

continued

№	$F(p, q)$	$f(x, y)$
1.169	$\frac{(pq)^n}{(pq)^n + a^n}$	$\frac{1}{n}\sum_{k=0}^{n-1} I_0\left(2\varepsilon^{k+\frac{1}{2}}\sqrt{axy}\right); \quad \varepsilon = e^{\frac{\pi i}{n}}$
1.170	$\sum_{k=0}^{n}(-1)^k\binom{n}{k}\times \times\sum_{i=0}^{k}\frac{1}{p^i q^{k-i}}$	$L_n(x+y)$
1.171	$\frac{pq}{p^m q^n + a}$	$\frac{x^{m-1}y^{n-1}}{(m-1)!\,(n-1)!}\,{}_1F_{m+n}\left(1;\ 1,\ 1+ +\frac{1}{m}, \ldots, 2-\frac{1}{m}, 1, 1+\frac{1}{n}, \ldots \ldots, 2-\frac{1}{n};\ -a\frac{x^m y^n}{m^m n^n}\right)$
1.172	$\frac{pq}{p^m q^n + a^m}$	$\frac{x^{\frac{m}{n}-1}}{na^{m\left(1-\frac{1}{n}\right)}}\sum_{k=0}^{\infty}\frac{\left(a^{\frac{m}{n}}x^{\frac{m}{n}}y\right)^k\varepsilon^{k-n+1}}{k!\,\Gamma\left[\frac{m}{n}(k+1)\right]}\times \times\frac{1-\varepsilon^{2n(k-n+1)}}{1-\varepsilon^{2(k-n+1)}}; \quad \varepsilon = e^{\frac{\pi i}{n}}$
1.173	$\frac{pq}{p^m q^n - a^m}$	$\frac{x^{\frac{m}{n}-1}}{na^{m\left(1-\frac{1}{n}\right)}}\times \times\sum_{k=0}^{\infty}\frac{\left(a^{\frac{m}{n}}x^{\frac{m}{n}}y\right)^k\left(1-\varepsilon^{n(k-n+1)}\right)}{k!\,\Gamma\left[\frac{m}{n}(k+1)\right]\left(1-\varepsilon^{k-n+1}\right)};$ $\varepsilon = e^{\frac{2\pi i}{n}}$

continued

№	$F(p, q)$	$f(x, y)$
1.174	$\frac{pq}{p^m q^n - a^n}$	$\frac{x^{\frac{m}{n}-1}}{na^{n-1}} \sum_{k=0}^{\infty} \frac{\left(ax^{\frac{m}{n}} y\right)^k}{k!\,\Gamma\left[\frac{m}{n}(k+1)\right]} \times$ $\times \frac{1 - \varepsilon^{n(k-n+1)}}{1 - \varepsilon^{k-n+1}}; \quad \varepsilon = e^{\frac{2\pi i}{n}}$
1.175	$\frac{p^m q^n}{p^m q^n - a^m}$	$\frac{1}{n} \sum_{k=0}^{\infty} \frac{\left(a^{\frac{m}{n}} x^{\frac{m}{n}} y\right)^k}{k!\,\Gamma\left(\frac{m}{n} k + 1\right)} \frac{1 - \varepsilon^{nk}}{1 - \varepsilon^k}; \quad \varepsilon = e^{\frac{2\pi i}{n}}$
1.176	$\frac{p^m q^n}{p^m q^n + a^m}$ $m, n > 0$	$\frac{1}{n} \sum_{k=0}^{\infty} \frac{\left(\varepsilon a^{\frac{m}{n}} x^{\frac{m}{n}} y\right)^k}{k!\,\Gamma\left[\frac{m}{n} k + 1\right]} \cdot \frac{1 - \varepsilon^{2nk}}{1 - \varepsilon^{2k}}; \quad \varepsilon = e^{\frac{\pi i}{n}}$
1.177	$\frac{p^{m-\alpha+1} q^{n-\beta+1}}{p^m q^n + a}$ α, β — positive integers	$\frac{x^{\alpha-1} y^{\beta-1}}{(\alpha-1)!\,(\beta-1)!} \times$ $\times {}_1F_{m+n}\left(1, \frac{\alpha}{m}, \frac{\alpha+1}{m}, \ldots, \frac{\alpha+m-1}{m},\right.$ $\left.\frac{\beta}{n}, \frac{\beta+1}{n}, \ldots, \frac{\beta+n-1}{n}; -\frac{ax^m y^n}{m^m n^n}\right)$
1.178	$\frac{p^{m-\alpha+1} q^{n-\beta+1}}{p^m q^n + a^m}$ α, β — positive integers	$\frac{x^{\alpha-1-\frac{m}{n}(\beta-1)}}{na^{\frac{m}{n}(\beta-1)}} \times$ $\times \sum_{k=0}^{\infty} \frac{\left(a^{\frac{m}{n}} x^{\frac{m}{n}} y\right)^k \varepsilon^{k-\beta+1}}{k!\,\Gamma\left[\frac{m}{n}(k-\beta+1)+\alpha\right]} \times$ $\times \frac{1 - \varepsilon^{2n(k-\beta+1)}}{1 - \varepsilon^{2(k-\beta+1)}}; \quad \varepsilon = e^{\frac{\pi i}{n}}$

continued

№	$F(p, q)$	$f(x, y)$
1.179	$\frac{p^{m-\alpha+1}q^{n-\beta+1}}{p^m q^n - a^m}$ α, β — positive integers	$\frac{x^{\alpha-1-\frac{m}{n}(\beta-1)}}{na^{\frac{m}{n}(\beta-1)}} \times$ $\times \sum_{k=0}^{\infty} \frac{\left(a^{\frac{m}{n}} x^{\frac{m}{n}} y\right)^k}{k!\,\Gamma\left[\frac{m}{n}(k-\beta+1)+\alpha\right]} \times$ $\times \frac{1-\varepsilon^{n(k-\beta+1)}}{1-\varepsilon^{k-\beta+1}}; \quad \varepsilon = e^{\frac{2\pi i}{n}}$
1.180	$\frac{pq^{m-n+1}}{(1+pq)^{m+1}}$	$\frac{x^{m-\frac{n}{2}} y^{\frac{n}{2}}}{\Gamma(m+1)} J_n(2\sqrt{xy})$
1.181	$\frac{p^2 q^2}{p^2+q^2+k^2}$ k — a real number	$\frac{1}{4} Y_0(\lvert k \rvert \sqrt{x^2+y^2})$
1.182	$\frac{1}{p^{\mu-k}q^{\nu-k}} \frac{1}{(p+q)^k}$ $\mu, \nu > -1$	$\frac{x^{\mu-k}}{\Gamma(\mu-k)} \cdot \frac{y^{\nu}}{\Gamma(\nu-1)} \times$ $\times {}_2F_1\left(k, k-\mu; \nu+1; \frac{y}{x}\right)$ for $y > x$; $\frac{x^{\mu}}{\Gamma(\mu+1)} \frac{y^{\nu-k}}{\Gamma(\nu-k)} \times$ $\times {}_2F_1\left(k, k-\nu; \mu+1; \frac{x}{y}\right)$ for $x > y$

continued

№	$F(p, q)$	$f(x, y)$
1.183	$\frac{q}{p^{\nu-1}(1+p^2q^2)} \times \times \left[pq\cos\frac{3\nu\pi}{4} - \sin\frac{3\nu\pi}{4}\right]$	$\left(\frac{x}{y}\right)^{\frac{1}{2}\nu} \operatorname{ber}_\nu(2\sqrt{xy})$
1.184	$\frac{q}{p^{\nu-1}(1+p^2q^2)} \times \times \left[\cos\frac{3\nu\pi}{4} + pq\sin\frac{3\nu\pi}{4}\right]$	$\left(\frac{x}{y}\right)^{\frac{1}{2}\nu} \operatorname{bei}_\nu(2\sqrt{xy})$
1.185	$\frac{1}{p^\nu}\frac{p^2q^2}{(1+p^2q^2)}$	$\left(\frac{x}{y}\right)^{\frac{1}{2}\nu}\left[\operatorname{ber}_\nu(2\sqrt{xy})\cos\frac{3\nu\pi}{4} + \operatorname{bei}_\nu(2\sqrt{xy})\sin\frac{3\nu\pi}{4}\right]$

IRRATIONAL FUNCTIONS

№	$F(p, q)$	$f(x, y)$
2.1	$\frac{pq\sqrt{p}}{pq+a}$	$\frac{1}{\sqrt{\pi x}}\cos(2\sqrt{axy})$
2.2	$\sqrt{pq}$	$\frac{1}{\pi\sqrt{xy}}$
2.3	$\frac{pq}{\sqrt{pq+a}}$	$\frac{1}{\pi\sqrt{xy}}\cos(2\sqrt{axy})$

continued

№	$F(p, q)$	$f(x, y)$
2.4	$\dfrac{pq}{p+\alpha\sqrt{q}}$ $\mid \arg\alpha \mid \leqslant \frac{\pi}{4}$, $\alpha \neq 0$	$\dfrac{\alpha x}{2\sqrt{\pi}\, y^{3/2}} e^{-\frac{\alpha^2 x^2}{4y}}$
2.5	$\dfrac{pq}{p+\sqrt{q}+q}$	$\begin{cases} \dfrac{x}{2\sqrt{\pi}\,(y-x)^{3/2}} e^{-\frac{x^2}{4(y-x)}} & \text{for } y > x; \\ 0 & \text{for } y < x \end{cases}$
2.6	$\dfrac{pq}{p+aq+\sqrt{cq+a}}$ $a \geqslant 0,\ c > 0$	$\begin{cases} \dfrac{1}{c} e^{-a\frac{y-ax}{c}} \dfrac{xc^{3/2}}{2\sqrt{\pi}\,(y-ax)^{3/2}} e^{-\frac{cx^2}{4(y-ax)}} & \text{for } y > ax; \\ 0 & \text{for } y < ax \end{cases}$
2.7	$\dfrac{pq}{\sqrt{p}(\sqrt{p}+\sqrt{q})}$	$\dfrac{1}{\pi}\sqrt{\dfrac{x}{y}}\dfrac{1}{x+y}$
2.8	$\dfrac{pq(q-\sqrt{q^2+1})}{p-q+\sqrt{q^2+1}}$	$\dfrac{x}{y+2x} J_2(\sqrt{y^2+2xy}) - \dfrac{1}{\sqrt{y^2+2xy}} J_1(\sqrt{y^2+2xy})$
2.9	$\dfrac{q}{\sqrt{p}+\sqrt{q}}$	$\dfrac{1}{\sqrt{\pi y}} - \dfrac{1}{\sqrt{\pi(x+y)}}$
2.10	$\dfrac{\sqrt{pq}}{\sqrt{p}+\sqrt{q}}$	$\dfrac{1}{\sqrt{\pi(x+y)}}$
2.11	$\dfrac{q\sqrt{p}}{(\sqrt{p}+\sqrt{q})^2}$	$\dfrac{x}{\sqrt{\pi}\,(x+y)^{3/2}}$

№	$F(p, q)$	$f(x, y)$
2.12	$\dfrac{p\sqrt{q}}{(p+a\sqrt{q})}$ $\lvert \arg a\rvert \leqslant \dfrac{\pi}{4}$	$\dfrac{e^{-\frac{a^2x^2}{4y}}}{\sqrt{\pi y}}$
2.13	$\dfrac{p\sqrt{q}}{p+q+\sqrt{q}}$	$\begin{cases} \dfrac{e^{-\frac{x^2}{4(y-x)}}}{\sqrt{\pi(y-x)}} & \text{for } y>x; \\ 0 & \text{for } y<x \end{cases}$
2.14	$\dfrac{q\sqrt{p}}{p+\sqrt{2pq}+q}$	$\dfrac{\sqrt{-y+\sqrt{x^2+y^2}}}{\sqrt{\pi}\sqrt{x^2+y^2}}$
2.15	$\dfrac{q\sqrt{p}}{p+\sqrt{2apq}+q}$ $a\geqslant 0$	$\dfrac{1}{\sqrt{\pi(2-a)}}\times$ $\times\dfrac{\sqrt{-(a-1)x-y+\sqrt{x^2+2(a-1)xy+y^2}}}{\sqrt{x^2+2(a-1)xy+y^2}}$
2.16	$\dfrac{q}{q+\sqrt{p}}$	$\operatorname{erfc}\left(\dfrac{y}{2\sqrt{x}}\right)$
2.17	$\dfrac{q}{p+\sqrt{pq}}$	$\dfrac{2}{\pi}\left[\sqrt{\dfrac{x}{y}}-\operatorname{arctg}\sqrt{\dfrac{x}{y}}\right]$
2.18	$\dfrac{p}{p+\sqrt{pq}}$	$\dfrac{2}{\pi}\operatorname{arctg}\sqrt{\dfrac{y}{x}}$
2.19	$\dfrac{q}{\sqrt{pq+a^2}}$	$\dfrac{1}{\pi a y}\sin(2a\sqrt{xy})$
2.20	$\dfrac{\sqrt{pq}}{(\sqrt{p}+\sqrt{q})^2}$	$\dfrac{2}{\pi}\dfrac{\sqrt{xy}}{x+y}$

continued

№	$F(p, q)$	$f(x, y)$
2.21	$\dfrac{q\sqrt{p}}{(\sqrt{p}+a)(\sqrt{p}+q)}$	$e^{a^2x+ay}\operatorname{erfc}\left(a\sqrt{x}+\dfrac{y}{2\sqrt{x}}\right)$
2.22	$\dfrac{p}{p-q+\sqrt{q^2+1}}$	$1-\displaystyle\int_0^y \dfrac{x}{\sqrt{\eta^2+2x\eta}} J_1(\sqrt{\eta^2+2x\eta})\,d\eta$
2.23	$\dfrac{pq}{p^2+1+(q-p)\sqrt{p^2+1}}$	$J_0(\sqrt{x^2+2xy})$
2.24	$\dfrac{p}{p-aq+\sqrt{c^2q^2+a^2}}$ $c \geqslant a$	$\begin{cases} 1-\displaystyle\int_0^{\frac{y-(c-a)x}{c}} \dfrac{ax}{\sqrt{\eta^2+2x\eta}}\times J_1(a\sqrt{\eta^2+2x\eta})\,d\eta & \text{for } y>(c-a)x; \\ 0 & \text{for } y<(c-a)x \end{cases}$
2.25	$\dfrac{p}{p+aq+\sqrt{c^2q^2+bq+a^2}}$ $a+c \geqslant 0$	$\begin{cases} e^{-\frac{b}{2c}x}-\sqrt{a^2-\dfrac{b^2}{4c^2}}\,x\times\displaystyle\int_0^{\frac{y-(a+c)x}{c}} \dfrac{e^{-\frac{b}{2c}(\eta+x)}}{\sqrt{\eta^2+2x\eta}}\times J_1\left(\sqrt{\left(a^2-\dfrac{b^2}{4c^2}\right)(\eta^2+2x\eta)}\right)d\eta & \text{for } y>(a+c)x; \\ 0 & \text{for } y<(a+c)x \end{cases}$
2.26	$\dfrac{pq}{\sqrt{p^2+1}\,(p+\sqrt{q^2+1})}$	$\begin{cases} J_0(\sqrt{y^2-x^2}) & \text{for } y>x; \\ 0 & \text{for } y<x \end{cases}$

continued

№	$F(p, q)$	$f(x, y)$
2.27	$\frac{pq}{\sqrt{c^2q^2+a^2}} \times \frac{1}{p+aq+b+\sqrt{c^2q^2+a^2}}$, $c>0,\ a+c\geqslant 0$	$\begin{cases} \frac{e^{-bx}}{c} J_0\left(\frac{a}{c}\sqrt{(y-ax)^2-c^2x^2}\right) & \text{for } y>(a+c)\,x; \\ 0 & \text{for } y<(a+c)\,x \end{cases}$
2.28	$\frac{pq}{\sqrt{c^2q^2+bq+a^2}} \times \frac{1}{p+\sqrt{c^2q^2+bq+a^2}}$, $c>0$	$\begin{cases} \frac{e^{-\frac{b}{2c^2}y}}{c} J_0\left(\frac{\sqrt{a^2-\frac{b^2}{4c^2}}}{c}\sqrt{y^2-c^2x^2}\right) & \text{for } y>cx; \\ 0 & \text{for } y<cx \end{cases}$
2.29	$\frac{pq}{\sqrt{c^2q^2+bq+a^2}} \times \frac{1}{(p-aq+d+\sqrt{c^2q^2+bq+a^2})}$, $c>0,\ c-a>0$	$\begin{cases} \frac{e^{-dx-\frac{b}{2c^2}(y+ax)}}{c} J_0\left(\frac{\sqrt{a^2-\frac{b^2}{4c^2}}}{c} \times \sqrt{(y+ax)^2-c^2x^2}\right) & \text{for } y>(c-a)\,x; \\ 0 & \text{for } y<(c-a)\,x \end{cases}$
2.30	$\frac{q\sqrt{q}}{p+\sqrt{2pq}+q}$	$\frac{1}{\sqrt{\pi y}}-\frac{1}{\sqrt{\pi}}\frac{\sqrt{x+\sqrt{x^2+y^2}}}{\sqrt{x^2+y^2}}$
2.31	$\frac{\sqrt{pq}\,(\sqrt{p}+\sqrt{2q})}{p+\sqrt{2pq}+q}$	$\frac{1}{\sqrt{\pi}}\frac{\sqrt{x+\sqrt{x^2+y^2}}}{\sqrt{x^2+y^2}}$
2.32	$\frac{\sqrt{pq}\left(\sqrt{p}+\frac{\sqrt{q}}{2}\right)}{(\sqrt{p}+\sqrt{q})^2}$	$\frac{1}{\sqrt{\pi(x+y)}}-\frac{\pi x}{2[\pi(x+y)]^{3/2}}$
2.33	$\frac{q\,(q-\sqrt{q^2+1})}{p-q+\sqrt{q^2+1}}$	$-\frac{x}{\sqrt{y^2+2xy}} J_1(\sqrt{y^2+2xy})$

continued

№	$F(p, q)$	$f(x, y)$
2.34	$pq\sqrt{\dfrac{\sqrt{p^2q^2+1}+1}{p^2q^2+1}}$	$\dfrac{1}{\pi\sqrt{xy}}[\operatorname{ch}\sqrt{2xy}\cos\sqrt{2xy}+ + \operatorname{sh}\sqrt{2xy}\cdot\sin\sqrt{2xy}]$
2.35	$pq\sqrt{\dfrac{\sqrt{p^2q^2-1}+i}{p^2q^2-1}}$	$\dfrac{1}{\pi\sqrt{xy}}\operatorname{ch}2\sqrt{xy}$
2.36	$pq\sqrt{\dfrac{\sqrt{p^2q^2-1}-i}{p^2q^2-1}}$	$\dfrac{1}{\pi\sqrt{xy}}\cos 2\sqrt{xy}$
2.37	$\sqrt{\dfrac{\sqrt{p^2q^2+1}+pq}{1+\dfrac{1}{p^2q^2}}}$	$\dfrac{1}{\pi}\sqrt{\dfrac{2}{xy}}\operatorname{ch}\sqrt{2xy}\cdot\cos\sqrt{2xy}$
2.38	$\sqrt{\dfrac{\sqrt{p^2q^2+1}-pq}{1+\dfrac{1}{p^2q^2}}}$	$\dfrac{1}{\pi}\sqrt{\dfrac{2}{xy}}\operatorname{sh}\sqrt{2xy}\cdot\sin\sqrt{2xy}$
2.39	$\sqrt{\dfrac{\sqrt{p^2q^2-1}+pq}{1-\dfrac{1}{p^2q^2}}}$	$\dfrac{1}{\pi\sqrt{2xy}}[\operatorname{ch}2\sqrt{xy}+\cos 2\sqrt{xy}]$
2.40	$\sqrt{\dfrac{\sqrt{p^2q^2-1}-pq}{1-\dfrac{1}{p^2q^2}}}$	$\dfrac{1}{\pi\sqrt{2xy}}[\operatorname{ch}2\sqrt{xy}-\cos 2\sqrt{xy}]$
2.41	$\dfrac{q\sqrt{p}}{pq+a}$	$\dfrac{1}{\sqrt{a\pi y}}\sin 2\sqrt{axy}$
2.42	$\dfrac{1}{\sqrt{pq}}\cdot\dfrac{q}{\sqrt{p}+\sqrt{q}}$	$\dfrac{2}{\sqrt{\pi}}[\sqrt{x+y}-\sqrt{y}]$
2.43	$\dfrac{\sqrt{q}}{p+\sqrt{q}}$	$\operatorname{erf}\left(\dfrac{x}{2\sqrt{y}}\right)$

continued

№	$F(p, q)$	$f(x, y)$
2.44	$\frac{1}{\sqrt{p}} \frac{q}{p+\sqrt{2pq}+q}$	$\frac{2}{\sqrt{\pi}}\left[\sqrt{y+\sqrt{x^2+y^2}}-\sqrt{2y}\right]$
2.45	$\frac{\sqrt{q}}{p+\sqrt{2pq}+q}$	$\frac{2}{\sqrt{\pi}}\left[\sqrt{y}-\sqrt{\sqrt{x^2+y^2}-x}\right]$
2.46	$\frac{p}{(p+q)(q+a\sqrt{q})}$ Re $a>0$	$\begin{cases} \frac{2}{a\sqrt{\pi}}\sqrt{y-x}- \\ \quad -\frac{1}{a}\int_x^y \chi[a(\eta-x),\ y-\eta]\,d\eta & \text{for } y>x; \\ 0 & \text{for } y<x \end{cases}$
2.47	$\frac{p\sqrt{q}}{(p+q)(q+a\sqrt{q})}$ Re $a>0$	$\begin{cases} \int_x^y \chi[a(\eta-x),\ y-\eta]\,d\eta & \text{for } y>x; \\ 0 & \text{for } y<x \end{cases}$
2.48	$\frac{q}{\sqrt{p}(\sqrt{p}+\sqrt{q})^2}$	$\frac{2}{\sqrt{\pi}}\left[\frac{x+2y}{\sqrt{x+y}}-2\sqrt{y}\right]$
2.49	$\frac{\sqrt{q}}{(\sqrt{p}+\sqrt{q})^2}$	$2\sqrt{\frac{y}{\pi}}\left[1-\sqrt{\frac{y}{x+y}}\right]$
2.50	$\frac{\sqrt{pq}}{(\sqrt{p}+\sqrt{q})^3}$	$\frac{1}{\sqrt{\pi}} \frac{xy}{(x+y)^{3/2}}$
2.51	$\frac{pq}{(pq+a)^{3/2}}$	$\frac{2}{\pi\sqrt{a}}\sin(2\sqrt{axy})$
2.52	$\frac{q}{p(q+\sqrt{p})}$	$xy^2\chi(y, x)+\left(x+\frac{y^2}{2}\right)\operatorname{erfc}\left(\frac{y}{2\sqrt{x}}\right)$

continued

№	$F(p, q)$	$f(x, y)$
2.53	$\dfrac{1}{(p+a\sqrt{p})\,q}$ $\operatorname{Re} a > 0$	$\dfrac{2}{a\sqrt{\pi}}\,y\sqrt{x} - \dfrac{1}{a}\,y\int\limits_0^x \chi(a\xi, x-\xi)\,d\xi$
2.54	$\dfrac{1}{\sqrt{(p+q)^2+1}}$	$\begin{cases} \int\limits_0^x J_0(\xi)\,d\xi & \text{for } y > x; \\ \int\limits_0^y J_0(\eta)\,d\eta & \text{for } y < x \end{cases}$
2.55	$\dfrac{p}{(p+q)\sqrt{(p+q)^2+1}}$	$\begin{cases} \int\limits_0^x J_0(\xi)\,d\xi & \text{for } y > x; \\ 0 & \text{for } y < x \end{cases}$
2.56	$\dfrac{pq(p+q)}{\sqrt{p^2+1}\sqrt{q^2+1}\times(\sqrt{p^2+1}+\sqrt{q^2+1})}$	$J_0(x+y)$
2.57	$\sqrt{\dfrac{p}{q}}\cdot\dfrac{\sqrt{p}+\sqrt{2q}}{p+\sqrt{2pq}+q}$	$\dfrac{2}{\sqrt{\pi}}\sqrt{\sqrt{x^2+y^2}-x}$
2.58	$\sqrt{\dfrac{q}{p}}\cdot\dfrac{\sqrt{p}+\sqrt{2q}}{p+\sqrt{2pq}+q}$	$\dfrac{2}{\sqrt{\pi}}\left[\sqrt{\sqrt{x^2+y^2}+x}-\sqrt{y}\right]$
2.59	$\sqrt{\dfrac{q}{p}}\;\dfrac{\sqrt{p}+\dfrac{\sqrt{q}}{2}}{(\sqrt{p}+\sqrt{q})^2}$	$\dfrac{x}{\sqrt{\pi(x+y)}}$
2.60	$\dfrac{pq(pq-p\sqrt{q^2+1}-1)}{(p+q)\sqrt{q^2+1}\times(p+\sqrt{q^2+1})}$	$\begin{cases} \dfrac{-y}{\sqrt{y^2-x^2}}J_1(\sqrt{y^2-x^2}) & \text{for } y > x; \\ 0 & \text{for } y < x \end{cases}$

continued

№	$F(p, q)$	$f(x, y)$
2.61	$\dfrac{1}{(p+2\sqrt{pq}+q+1)^{3/2}}$	$\dfrac{2}{\pi}\dfrac{\sqrt{xy}}{x+y}e^{\frac{xy}{x+y}}$
2.62	$\dfrac{pq(p+q)}{\sqrt{p^2+1}\sqrt{q^2+1}\times(p\sqrt{q^2+1}+q\sqrt{p^2+1})}$	$J_1(x+y)$
2.63	$\dfrac{1}{\sqrt{pq}}\left[\sqrt{2q}+\dfrac{p\sqrt{p}}{p+\sqrt{2pq}+q}\right]$	$\dfrac{2}{\sqrt{\pi}}\sqrt{x+\sqrt{x^2+y^2}}$
2.64	$\dfrac{pq^2(p+2\sqrt{q^2+1})}{(q^2+1)^{3/2}(p+\sqrt{q^2+1})^2}$	$\begin{cases} yJ_0(\sqrt{y^2-x^2}) & \text{for } y>x; \\ 0 & \text{for } y<x \end{cases}$
2.65	$\dfrac{pq^{\nu+1}}{p+\sqrt{q}}$ $\operatorname{Re}\nu<\dfrac{1}{2}$	$\sqrt{\dfrac{2}{\pi}}\dfrac{e^{-\frac{x^2}{8y}}}{(2y)^{\nu+1}}D_{2\nu+1}\left(\dfrac{x}{\sqrt{2y}}\right)$
2.66	$\dfrac{q}{p^{\nu-1}(p+q)}$ $\operatorname{Re}\nu>0$	0 for $y>x$; $\dfrac{(x-y)^{\nu-1}}{\Gamma(\nu)}$ for $y<x$
2.67	$\dfrac{q}{p^{\nu-1}(pq+a)}$ $\operatorname{Re}\nu>-1$	$\left(\dfrac{x}{ay}\right)^{\frac{\nu}{2}}J_\nu(2\sqrt{axy})$
2.68	$\dfrac{q}{p^{\nu-1}(p^2q^2+a^2)}$ $\operatorname{Re}\nu>-2$	$\dfrac{1}{a}\left(\dfrac{x}{ay}\right)^{\frac{\nu}{2}}\left[\cos\dfrac{3\nu\pi}{4}\operatorname{bei}_\nu(2\sqrt{axy})-\sin\dfrac{3\nu\pi}{4}\operatorname{ber}_\nu(2\sqrt{axy})\right]$

continued

№	$F(p, q)$	$f(x, y)$
2.69	$\dfrac{q}{p^{\nu-1}(p^2q^2-a^2)}$ $\operatorname{Re}\nu>-2$	$\dfrac{1}{2a}\left(\dfrac{x}{ay}\right)^{\frac{\nu}{2}}[I_\nu(2\sqrt{axy})-J_\nu(2\sqrt{axy})]$
2.70	$\dfrac{p^2q^2}{p^\nu(p^2q^2+a^2)}$ $\operatorname{Re}\nu>-1$	$\left(\dfrac{x}{ay}\right)^{\frac{\nu}{2}}\left[\cos\dfrac{3\nu\pi}{4}\operatorname{ber}_\nu(2\sqrt{axy})+\right.$ $\left.+\sin\dfrac{3\nu\pi}{4}\operatorname{bei}_\nu(2\sqrt{axy})\right]$
2.71	$\dfrac{p^2q^2}{p^\nu(p^2q^2-a^2)}$ $\operatorname{Re}\nu>-1$	$\dfrac{1}{2}\left(\dfrac{x}{ay}\right)^{\frac{\nu}{2}}[J_\nu(2\sqrt{axy})+I_\nu(2\sqrt{axy})]$
2.72	$\dfrac{p^2q^2\sin\dfrac{3\nu\pi}{4}+apq\cos\dfrac{3\nu\pi}{4}}{p^\nu(p^2q^2+a^2)}$ $\operatorname{Re}\nu>-1$	$\left(\dfrac{x}{ay}\right)^{\frac{\nu}{2}}\operatorname{bei}_\nu(2\sqrt{axy})$
2.73	$\dfrac{p^2q^2\cos\dfrac{3\nu\pi}{4}-apq\sin\dfrac{3\nu\pi}{4}}{p^\nu(p^2q^2+a^2)}$ $\operatorname{Re}\nu>-1$	$\left(\dfrac{x}{ay}\right)^{\frac{\nu}{2}}\operatorname{ber}_\nu(2\sqrt{axy})$
2.74	$\dfrac{pq}{(pq+a)^\nu}$ $\operatorname{Re}\nu>0$	$\dfrac{1}{\Gamma(\nu)}\left(\dfrac{xy}{a}\right)^{\frac{\nu-1}{2}}J_{\nu-1}(2\sqrt{axy})$
2.75	$\dfrac{pq}{[(p+1)(q+1)+apq]^\nu}$ $\operatorname{Re}\nu>0,\ \|a\|<1$	$\dfrac{1}{\Gamma(\nu)}\dfrac{e^{-\frac{x+y}{a+1}}}{a+1}\left(\dfrac{xy}{a}\right)^{\frac{\nu-1}{2}}J_{\nu-1}\left(\dfrac{2\sqrt{axy}}{a+1}\right)$
2.76	$\dfrac{p\sqrt{q}}{\sqrt{pq+aq+1}}$	$\dfrac{e^{-ax}}{\sqrt{\pi x}}J_0(2\sqrt{xy})$

continued

№	$F(p, q)$	$f(x, y)$
2.77	$\frac{\pi\sqrt{pq}}{2(\sqrt{p}+\sqrt{q})^2}$	$\frac{\sqrt{xy}}{x+y}$
2.78	$\frac{pq\sqrt{q}}{(pq+1)\sqrt{pq+aq+1}}$	$\frac{1}{\sqrt{a}}\operatorname{erf}(\sqrt{ax})\,J_0(2\sqrt{xy})$
2.79	$\frac{pq}{[ap^2+2bpq+cq^2+2dp+2eq+f]^{\nu}}$, $b>0,\ a,\ c\geqslant 0$, $b^2-ac>0,\ \operatorname{Re}\nu>0$	$\frac{1}{\Gamma(\nu)}\frac{1}{2^{\nu}D}e^{-\frac{be-cd}{D^2}x-\frac{bd-ae}{D^2}y}\times\left[\frac{cx^2-2bxy+ay^2}{2bde+acf-b^2f-cd^2-ae^2}\right]^{\frac{\nu-1}{2}}\times J_{\nu-1}\left[\frac{1}{D^2}\sqrt{(cx^2-2bxy+ay^2)\times(2bde+acf-b^2f-cd^2-ae^2)}\right]$ for $(b-D)x<ay<(b+D)x$, 0 otherwise $D=\sqrt{b^2-ac}$
2.80	$\frac{p}{(p+q)^{\nu}}$ $\operatorname{Re}\nu>0$	$\frac{x^{\nu-1}}{\Gamma(\nu)}$ for $y>x$, 0 for $y<x$
2.81	$\frac{1}{(p+q)^{\nu}}$ $\operatorname{Re}\nu>-1$	$\frac{x^{\nu}}{\Gamma(\nu+1)}$ for $y>x$, $\frac{y^{\nu}}{\Gamma(\nu+1)}$ for $y<x$
2.82	$\frac{1}{(p+q+a)^{\nu}}$ $\operatorname{Re}\nu>0$	$\int_0^x e^{-a\xi}\frac{\xi^{\nu-1}}{\Gamma(\nu)}d\xi$ for $y>x$, $\int_0^y e^{-a\eta}\frac{\eta^{\nu-1}}{\Gamma(\nu)}d\eta$ for $y<x$

continued

№	$F(p, q)$	$f(x, y)$
2.83	$\frac{q}{p^{n-1}(pq+a)^{\nu}}$ $\operatorname{Re}\nu>0$	$\frac{y^{\nu-1}}{\Gamma(\nu)}\left(\frac{x}{ay}\right)^{\frac{\nu+n-1}{2}} J_{\nu+n-1}(2\sqrt{axy})$
2.84	$\frac{q}{p^{\nu-1}(pq+1)^{\nu}}$ $\operatorname{Re}\nu>0$	$\frac{1}{\Gamma(\nu)}\frac{x^{\nu}}{\sqrt{xy}} J_{2\nu-1}(2\sqrt{xy})$
2.85	$\frac{q}{p^{\nu-1}(pq+1)^{\nu+1}}$ $\operatorname{Re}\nu>-\frac{1}{2}$	$\frac{x^{\nu}}{\Gamma(\nu+1)} J_{2\nu}(2\sqrt{xy})$
2.86	$\frac{pq}{p^{\nu+n}(pq+1)^{\nu+1}}$ $\operatorname{Re}\nu>-1$ for $n=1, 2, 3, \ldots,$ $\operatorname{Re}\nu>-\frac{1}{2}$ for $n=0$	$\frac{x^{\nu}}{\Gamma(\nu+1)}\left(\frac{x}{y}\right)^{\frac{n}{2}} J_{2\nu+n}(2\sqrt{xy})$
2.87	$\frac{1}{p^{\mu-1}q^{\nu-1}}$ $\operatorname{Re}\mu, \nu>0$	$\frac{x^{\mu-1}y^{\nu-1}}{\Gamma(\mu)\Gamma(\nu)}$
2.88	$\frac{pq}{(p-a)^{\mu}(q-b)^{\nu}}$ $\operatorname{Re}\mu, \nu>0$	$e^{ax+by}\frac{x^{\mu-1}y^{\nu-1}}{\Gamma(\mu)\Gamma(\nu)}$
2.89	$\left[\frac{1}{p^{\nu}}-\frac{1}{(p+q)^{\nu}}+\frac{1}{q^{\nu}}\right]$ $\operatorname{Re}\nu>-1$	$\begin{cases}\frac{y^{\nu}}{\Gamma(\nu+1)} & \text{for } y>x,\\ \frac{x^{\nu}}{\Gamma(\nu+1)} & \text{for } y<x\end{cases}$

continued

№	$F(p, q)$	$f(x, y)$
2.90	$\dfrac{p^{\nu}+q^{\nu}}{(pq)^{\nu}}$ $\operatorname{Re}\nu>-1$	$\dfrac{x^{\nu}+y^{\nu}}{\Gamma(\nu+1)}$
2.91	$\dfrac{p^{\nu}q}{(pq+a)^{\nu}}$ $\operatorname{Re}\nu>0$	$\dfrac{y^{\nu-1}}{\Gamma(\nu)}J_0(2\sqrt{axy})$
2.92	$\dfrac{p^{\nu}-q^{\nu}}{p^{\nu-1}q^{\nu-1}(p-q)}$ $\operatorname{Re}\nu>0$	$\dfrac{(x+y)^{\nu-1}}{\Gamma(\nu)}$
2.93	$pq\dfrac{(pq+1)^{\nu}+(pq-1)^{\nu}}{(p^2q^2-1)^{\nu}}$ $\operatorname{Re}\nu>0$	$\dfrac{(xy)^{\frac{\nu-1}{2}}}{\Gamma(\nu)}[J_{\nu-1}(2\sqrt{xy})+I_{\nu-1}(2\sqrt{xy})]$
2.94	$pq\dfrac{(pq+1)^{\nu}-(pq-1)^{\nu}}{(p^2q^2-1)^{\nu}}$ $\operatorname{Re}\nu>0$	$\dfrac{(xy)^{\frac{\nu-1}{2}}}{\Gamma(\nu)}[I_{\nu-1}(2\sqrt{xy})-J_{\nu-1}(2\sqrt{xy})]$
2.95	$pq\dfrac{(p+\sqrt{p^2-q})^{\nu}-(p-\sqrt{p^2-q})^{\nu}}{\sqrt{p^2-q}}$ $\lvert\operatorname{Re}\nu\rvert<1$	$\dfrac{\sin\nu\pi}{2^{\nu}\pi}\cdot\dfrac{x^{\nu}e^{-\frac{x^2}{4y}}}{y^{\nu+1}}$
2.96	$pq\dfrac{(p+\sqrt{p^2-q^2})^{\nu}-(p-\sqrt{p^2-q^2})^{\nu}}{q^{\nu}\sqrt{p^2-q^2}}$ $\lvert\operatorname{Re}\nu\rvert<1$	$\begin{cases}\dfrac{\sin\nu\pi}{\pi}\times\dfrac{(y+\sqrt{y^2-x^2})^{\nu}+(y-\sqrt{y^2-x^2})^{\nu}}{x^{\nu}\sqrt{y^2-x^2}} & \text{for } y>x,\\ 0 & \text{for } y<x\end{cases}$

continued

№	$F(p, q)$	$f(x, y)$
2.97	$\dfrac{pq\,[1+(q-1)\,p]^n}{p^{\nu-a}\,(pq+1)^{n+a+1}}$ Re ν, $a>-1$	$\dfrac{n!\,y^a}{\Gamma(n+a+1)}\left(\dfrac{x}{y}\right)^{\frac{\nu}{2}} J_\nu(2\sqrt{xy})\;L_n^{(a)}(y)$
2.98	$\dfrac{pq}{(p^2+q^2+k^2)}\times\left[\dfrac{p}{\sqrt{p^2+k^2}}+\dfrac{q}{\sqrt{p^2+k^2}}\right]$	$J_0(k\sqrt{x^2+y^2})$
2.99	$\dfrac{\sqrt{pq}}{(\sqrt{p}+\sqrt{q})^{\nu+1}}$	$\dfrac{(xy)^{\frac{\nu}{2}}}{\sqrt{\pi}\,\Gamma\left(\dfrac{\nu}{2}+1\right)(x+y)^{\frac{\nu+1}{2}}}$
2.100	$\dfrac{(p-1)^n q^n-(q-1)^n p^n}{(q-p)p^{n-1}q^{n-1}}$	$L'_n(x+y)$
2.101	$\left(1-\dfrac{1}{2p}-\dfrac{1}{2q}\right)^m$	$L_m\left(\dfrac{x}{2},\dfrac{y}{2}\right)$*)
2.102	$\dfrac{1}{\sqrt{pq}}\left(\dfrac{1}{p}+\dfrac{1}{q}-1\right)^m$	$\dfrac{m!}{\pi\,(2m+1)!}H_{2m+1}(\sqrt{x},\sqrt{y})$ *
2.103	$\sqrt{pq}\left(\dfrac{1}{p}+\dfrac{1}{q}-1\right)^m$	$\dfrac{m!}{\pi\,(2m)!}\;\dfrac{H_{2m}(\sqrt{x},\sqrt{y})}{\sqrt{xy}}$ *
2.104	$\dfrac{1}{p^\alpha q^\beta}\left(1-\dfrac{1}{p}-\dfrac{1}{q}\right)^m$	$\dfrac{(m!)^2\,x^\alpha y^\beta\,L_m^{\alpha,\beta}(x,y)}{\Gamma(m+\alpha+1)\,\Gamma(m+\beta+1)}$ *
2.105	$\dfrac{\sqrt{pq}(\sqrt{p}+\sqrt{q})}{\sqrt{1+(\sqrt{p}+\sqrt{q})^2}}$	$\dfrac{1}{\pi\sqrt{xy}}\,e^{-\frac{xy}{x+y}}$

* $L_m(x, y)$, $H_m(x, y)$, $L_m^{\alpha,\beta}(x, y)$ are introduced here by analogy with the universally adopted notations for the corresponding polynomials in one variable.

continued

№	$F(p, q)$	$f(x, y)$
2.106	$\frac{\sqrt{pq}}{(\sqrt{p}+\sqrt{q})^{\nu+1}}$	$\frac{(xy)^{\frac{\nu}{2}}}{\sqrt{\pi}\,\Gamma\left(\frac{\nu}{2}+1\right)(x+y)^{\frac{\nu+1}{2}}}$
2.107	$\frac{\sqrt{pq}(\sqrt{p}+\sqrt{q})}{(\sqrt{p}+\sqrt{q})^4+1}$	$\frac{1}{\sqrt{\pi(x+y)}}\sin\frac{xy}{x+y}$
2.108	$\frac{\sqrt{pq}(\sqrt{p}+\sqrt{q})^3}{(\sqrt{p}+\sqrt{q})^4+1}$	$\frac{1}{\sqrt{\pi(x+y)}}\cos\frac{xy}{x+y}$
2.109	$\frac{\sqrt{pq}\,(\sqrt{p}+\sqrt{q})}{[(\sqrt{p}+\sqrt{q})^2+1]^{3/2}}$	$\frac{2}{\pi}\frac{\sqrt{xy}}{(x+y)}e^{-\frac{xy}{x+y}}$
2.110	$\frac{pq[\sqrt{p^2q^2+1}-pq]}{\sqrt{p^2q^2+1}}$	$J_0(2\sqrt{xy})\,I_1(2\sqrt{xy})$
2.111	$\sqrt{\frac{pq}{pq+1}}$	$J_0^2(\sqrt{xy})$
2.112	$\frac{\pi pq}{\sqrt{pq+1}}$	$\frac{\cos 2\sqrt{xy}}{\sqrt{xy}}$
2.113	$\Gamma(\nu+1)\cdot\frac{p^{\mu(\nu+1)-\lambda}\cdot q}{(1+p^{\mu}q)^{\nu+1}}$ $\operatorname{Re}\nu>-1$	$x^{\lambda}y^{\nu}J_{\lambda}^{\mu}(x^{\mu}y)=\sum_{r=0}^{\infty}\frac{(-1)^r x^{\lambda+\mu r}y^{\nu+r}}{r!\,\Gamma(1+\lambda+\mu r)}$
2.114	$\frac{\pi\Gamma(2n+2)}{\Gamma(n+1)}\times$ $\times\frac{pq^{n+1}}{(4pq+1)^{n+\frac{3}{2}}}$	$x^n\sin\sqrt{xy}$

continued

№	$F(p, q)$	$f(x, y)$
2.115	$\frac{2\pi\Gamma(2n+1)}{\Gamma(n+1)} \times$ $\times \frac{pq^{n+1}}{(4pq+1)^{n+\frac{1}{2}}}$	$\frac{x^n \cos\sqrt{xy}}{\sqrt{xy}}$
2.116	$\frac{p\sqrt{q}}{\sqrt{p+\sqrt{q}}}$	$\frac{e^{-\frac{x^2}{4y}}}{\pi\sqrt{xy}}$
2.117	$\left(\frac{q}{p}\right)^{\alpha} \frac{\sqrt{pq}}{\sqrt{pq+1}}$	$\left(\frac{x}{y}\right)^{\alpha} J_{\alpha}(\sqrt{xy}) J_{-\alpha}(\sqrt{xy})$
2.118	$\frac{p^{\frac{1}{2}} q^{\frac{1}{2}-\alpha}}{(pq+1)^{\frac{1}{2}+\alpha}}$	$\frac{\sqrt{\pi}}{\Gamma\left(\frac{1}{2}+\alpha\right)} y^{\alpha} J_{\alpha}^2(\sqrt{xy})$

EXPONENTIAL FUNCTIONS

№	$F(p, q)$	$f(x, y)$
3.1	$p\left(1-e^{-\frac{1}{p+q}}\right)$	$\begin{cases} \frac{1}{\sqrt{x}} J_1(2\sqrt{x}) & \text{for } y > x, \\ 0 & \text{for } y < x \end{cases}$
3.2	$\frac{pq\left(e^{-\frac{1}{p}} - e^{-\frac{1}{q}}\right)}{p-q}$	$\frac{1}{\sqrt{x+y}} J_1(2\sqrt{x+y})$

continued

№	$F(p, q)$	$f(x, y)$
3.3	$e^{-\frac{1}{p+q}}$	$\begin{cases} J_0(2\sqrt{x}) & \text{for } y > x, \\ J_0(2\sqrt{y}) & \text{for } y < x \end{cases}$
3.4	$e^{\frac{1}{pq}}$	$J_{0,0}\left(-3\sqrt[3]{xy}\right)$
3.5	$e^{-\frac{1}{pq}}$	$J_{0,0}\left(3\sqrt[3]{xy}\right)$
3.6	$\frac{q(e^{-p}-e^{-q})}{p-q}$	$\begin{cases} -1 & \text{for } 1-x<y<1, \\ 0 & \text{otherwise} \end{cases}$
3.7	$\frac{q\left(e^{-\frac{1}{p}}-e^{-\frac{1}{q}}\right)}{p-q}$	$J_0(2\sqrt{y})-J_0(2\sqrt{x+y})$
3.8	$\frac{pq}{(p-a)}\frac{(e^{-(p-a)}-e^{-(q-b)})}{(p-a)-(q-b)}$	$\begin{cases} -e^{ax+by} & \text{for } 1-x<y<1, \\ 0 & \text{otherwise} \end{cases}$
3.9	$-\frac{e^{-p}-e^{-q}}{p-q}$.	$\begin{cases} 1 & \text{for } y>1 \text{ и } x>1, \\ x & \text{for } y>1 \text{ и } x<1, \\ y & \text{for } y<1 \text{ и } x>1, \\ x+y-1 & \text{for } 1-x<y<1 \text{ or } x<1, \\ 0 & \text{for } y<1-x \end{cases}$
3.10	$\frac{qe^{-ap}-pe^{-aq}}{p-q}$ $(a \geqslant 0)$	$\begin{cases} -1 & \text{for } y>a-x, \\ 0 & \text{for } y<a-x \end{cases}$
3.11	$\frac{q}{p}\cdot\frac{e^{-p}-e^{-q}}{p-q}$	$\begin{cases} 1-x-y & \text{for } 1-x<y<1, \\ 0 & \text{otherwise} \end{cases}$
3.12	$\frac{pe^{-\frac{1}{q}}-qe^{-\frac{1}{p}}}{p-q}$	$J_0(2\sqrt{x+y})$
3.13	$\frac{q[e^{-n\pi p}-(-1)^n e^{-n\pi q}]}{(p-q)^2+1}$	$\begin{cases} \sin y & \text{for } n\pi-x<y<n\pi, \\ 0 & \text{otherwise} \end{cases}$

continued

№	$F(p, q)$	$f(x, y)$
3.14	$\dfrac{q(q-p)\left[e^{-n\pi p}-(-1)^n e^{-n\pi q}\right]}{(p-q)^2+1}$	$\begin{cases} \cos y & \text{for } n\pi - x < y < n\pi, \\ 0 & \text{otherwise} \end{cases}$
3.15	$\dfrac{pq(q-2p)}{p^2+1} \times \dfrac{\left[(-1)^n e^{-n\pi p}-e^{-n\pi q}\right]}{(p-q)^2+1}$	$\begin{cases} \sin x & \text{for } n\pi - x < y < n\pi, \\ 0 & \text{otherwise} \end{cases}$
3.16	$\dfrac{pq(1+pq-p^2)}{p^2+1} \times \dfrac{\left[(-1)^n e^{-n\pi p}-e^{-n\pi q}\right]}{(p-q)^2+1}$	$\begin{cases} \cos x & \text{for } n\pi - x < y < n\pi, \\ 0 & \text{otherwise} \end{cases}$
3.17	$\dfrac{q\left[e^{-\left(n+\frac{1}{2}\right)\pi p}-(-1)^n (q-p)\, e^{-\left(n+\frac{1}{2}\right)\pi q}\right]}{(p-q)^2+1}$	$\begin{cases} \sin y & \text{for } \left(n+\frac{1}{2}\right)\pi - x < y < \left(n+\frac{1}{2}\right)\pi, \\ 0 & \text{otherwise} \end{cases}$
3.18	$\dfrac{q\left[(q-p)\, e^{-\left(n+\frac{1}{2}\right)\pi p}+(-1)^n e^{-\left(n+\frac{1}{2}\right)\pi q}\right]}{(p-q)^2+1}$	$\begin{cases} \cos y & \text{for } \left(n+\frac{1}{2}\right)\pi - x < y < \left(n+\frac{1}{2}\right)\pi, \\ 0 & \text{otherwise} \end{cases}$
3.19	$\dfrac{pq\left[(-1)^n (1+pq-p^2)\, e^{-\left(n+\frac{1}{2}\right)\pi p}-(q-2p)\, e^{-\left(n+\frac{1}{2}\right)\pi q}\right]}{(p^2+1)\left[(p-q)^2+1\right]}$	$\begin{cases} \sin x & \text{for } \left(n+\frac{1}{2}\right)\pi - x < y < \left(n+\frac{1}{2}\right)\pi, \\ 0 & \text{otherwise} \end{cases}$
3.20	$\dfrac{-pq\left[(-1)^n (q-2p)\, e^{-\left(n+\frac{1}{2}\right)\pi p}+(1+pq-p^2)\, e^{-\left(n+\frac{1}{2}\right)\pi q}\right]}{(p^2+1)\left[(p-q)^2+1\right]}$	$\begin{cases} \cos x & \text{for } \left(n+\frac{1}{2}\right)\pi - x < y < \left(n+\frac{1}{2}\right)\pi, \\ 0 & \text{otherwise} \end{cases}$

continued

№	$F(p, q)$	$f(x, y)$
3.21	$\sqrt{pq}e^{-\sqrt{pq}}$	$\begin{cases} \dfrac{2}{\pi\sqrt{4xy-1}} & \text{for } y > \dfrac{1}{4x}, \\ 0 & \text{for } y < \dfrac{1}{4x} \end{cases}$
3.22	$\dfrac{q}{\sqrt{p}} e^{-\sqrt{pq}}$	$\begin{cases} \dfrac{1}{2\sqrt{\pi}y^{3/2}} & \text{for } y > \dfrac{1}{4x}, \\ 0 & \text{for } y < \dfrac{1}{4x} \end{cases}$
3.23	$\sqrt{p}e^{-\sqrt{pq}}$	$\begin{cases} \dfrac{1}{\sqrt{\pi x}} & \text{for } y > \dfrac{1}{4x}, \\ 0 & \text{for } y < \dfrac{1}{4x} \end{cases}$
3.24	$\dfrac{qe^{-\sqrt{pq}}}{p^{\nu-1}}$ $\operatorname{Re} \nu > \dfrac{1}{2}$	$\begin{cases} \dfrac{\left(x-\dfrac{1}{4y}\right)^{\nu-\frac{3}{2}}}{2\sqrt{\pi}\Gamma\left(\nu-\dfrac{1}{2}\right)y^{3/2}} & \text{for } y > \dfrac{1}{4x}, \\ 0 & \text{for } y < \dfrac{1}{4x} \end{cases}$
3.25	$\dfrac{\sqrt{q}e^{-\sqrt{pq}}}{p^{\nu-1}}$ $\operatorname{Re} \nu > 0$	$\begin{cases} \dfrac{1}{\Gamma(\nu)\sqrt{\pi y}}\left(x-\dfrac{1}{4y}\right)^{\nu-1} & \text{for } y > \dfrac{1}{4x}, \\ 0 & \text{for } y < \dfrac{1}{4x} \end{cases}$
3.26	$\dfrac{1}{\sqrt{p}} \dfrac{e^{-\frac{1}{\sqrt{pq}}}}{(pq)^{\nu-1}}$ $\operatorname{Re} \nu > 0$	$\dfrac{(4xy)^{\frac{2\nu-1}{4}}}{\sqrt{\pi y}} J_{2\nu-1}\left[2(4xy)^{\frac{1}{4}}\right]$

continued

№	$F(p, q)$	$f(x, y)$
3.27	$\dfrac{pe^{-p}}{p+\ln q}$	$\begin{cases} \dfrac{y^{x-1}}{\Gamma(x)} & \text{for } x>1, \\ 0 & \text{for } x<1 \end{cases}$
3.28	$\dfrac{p}{q^n}\,\dfrac{q-e^{-p}}{p+\ln q}$ $n>0$	$\begin{cases} 0 & \text{for } x>1, \\ \dfrac{y^{x+n-1}}{\Gamma(x+n)} & \text{for } x<1 \end{cases}$
3.29	$\dfrac{1}{(pq)^{n-1}}\,e^{-\frac{1}{pq}}$	$(xy)^{\frac{n-1}{3}} J_{n-1,\,n-1}\left(3\sqrt[3]{xy}\right)$
3.30	$-\dfrac{1}{(pq)^n}\ln(pq)\,e^{-\frac{1}{pq}}$	$\dfrac{1}{3}(xy)^{\frac{n}{3}}\ln(xy)\,J_{n,\,n}\left(3\sqrt[3]{xy}\right)+$ $+(xy)^{\frac{n}{3}}\dfrac{d}{dn}J_{n,\,n}\left(3\sqrt[3]{xy}\right)$
3.31	$\dfrac{e^{-\frac{1}{pq}}}{p^m q^n}$	$x^{\frac{2m-n}{3}}\,y^{\frac{2n-m}{3}}\,J_{m,\,n}\left(3\sqrt[3]{xy}\right)$
3.32	$e^{\frac{1}{p^2q}}$	$\mathrm{ber}^2\left(2\sqrt{x\sqrt{y}}\right)+\mathrm{bei}^2\left(2\sqrt{x\sqrt{y}}\right)$
3.33	$\sqrt{\dfrac{\pi}{2}}\,e^{-\frac{1}{4p^2q}}$	$\mathrm{bei}\left(2\sqrt{x\sqrt{2y}}\right)$
3.34	$\sqrt{\pi q}\,e^{-\frac{1}{4p^2q}}$	$\dfrac{1}{\sqrt{y}}\,\mathrm{ber}\left(2\sqrt{x\sqrt{2y}}\right)$
3.35	$\pi\sqrt{2pq}\,e^{-2\sqrt{q\sqrt{p}}}$	$\dfrac{1}{\sqrt{xy}}\,e^{-\frac{1}{xy^2}}$

continued

№	$F(p, q)$	$f(x, y)$
3.36	$\pi 2^{\frac{1}{4}-\mu} p^{\frac{1}{4}-\mu} \times$ $\times q^{\frac{1}{2}} e^{-2\sqrt{q\sqrt{p}}}$	$x^{\mu-\frac{1}{4}} y^{-\frac{1}{2}} e^{-\frac{1}{2xy^2}} D_{-2\mu-\frac{1}{2}}\left(\sqrt{\frac{2}{xy^2}}\right)$
3.37	$\frac{(m+1)pq-1}{p^{m+2}q^{n+1}} e^{-\frac{1}{pq}}$	$x^{\frac{2m-n}{3}+1} y^{\frac{2n-m}{3}} J_{m,n}(3\sqrt[3]{xy})$

LOGARITHMIC FUNCTIONS

№	$F(p, q)$	$f(x, y)$
4.1	$q \ln\left(1+\frac{p}{q}\right)$	$\begin{cases} \frac{1}{y} & \text{for } y > x, \\ 0 & \text{for } y < x \end{cases}$
4.2	$p\sqrt{q} \ln \frac{p+\sqrt{q}-a}{p+\sqrt{q}}$	$\frac{e^{-\frac{x^2}{4y}}}{x\sqrt{\pi y}}(1-e^{ax})$
4.3	$\frac{pq}{p-q} \ln \frac{q}{p}$	$\frac{1}{x+y}$
4.4	$\ln(p+q)$	$\begin{cases} \Gamma'(1)-\ln x & \text{for } y > x \\ \Gamma'(1)-\ln y & \text{for } y < x \end{cases}$
4.5	$\ln(p+q+1)$	$-\mathrm{Ei}(-x)$ for $y > x$ $-\mathrm{Ei}(-y)$ for $y < x$
4.6	$\ln pq$	$2\Gamma'(1)-\ln(xy)$

continued

№	$F(p, q)$	$f(x, y)$
4.7	$\ln(pq + a)$	$2Ji_0(2\sqrt{axy}) + \ln a$
4.8	$\ln[(p+1)(q+1)]$	$-\mathrm{Ei}(-x) - \mathrm{Ei}(-y)$
4.9	$\ln \frac{(p+1)(q+1)}{p+q+1}$	$-\mathrm{Ei}(-y)$ for $y > x$, $-\mathrm{Ei}(-x)$ for $y < x$
4.10	$\ln \frac{(p+1)(q+1)}{(p+q+1)^2}$	$\begin{cases} \mathrm{Ei}(-x) - \mathrm{Ei}(-y) & \text{for } y > x, \\ \mathrm{Ei}(-y) - \mathrm{Ei}(-x) & \text{for } y < x \end{cases}$
4.11	$\frac{p \ln(p+q)}{p+q}$	$\begin{cases} \Gamma'(1) - \ln x & \text{for } y > x, \\ 0 & \text{for } y < x \end{cases}$
4.12	$\frac{q \ln p - p \ln q}{p - q}$	$\ln(x+y) - \Gamma'(1)$
4.13	$\frac{p^2 \ln \frac{p}{q} + \frac{\pi}{2} pq}{p^2 + q^2}$	$\ln \sqrt{1 + \left(\frac{y}{x}\right)^2}$
4.14	$\frac{pq \ln \frac{q}{p} + \frac{\pi}{2} p^2}{p^2 + q^2}$	$\mathrm{arctg}\, \frac{y}{x}$
4.15	$\Gamma'(1) - \ln p + \frac{p^2 \ln \frac{p}{q} + pq \frac{\pi}{2}}{p^2 + q^2}$	$\ln \sqrt{x^2 + y^2}$
4.16	$\frac{pq}{\sqrt{p^2+q^2}} \times \ln \frac{p+q+\sqrt{p^2+q^2}}{p+q-\sqrt{p^2+q^2}}$	$\frac{1}{\sqrt{x^2+y^2}}$

continued

№	$F(p, q)$	$f(x, y)$
4.17	$\frac{pq}{\sqrt{p^2+q^2-a^2}} \times \ln \frac{p+q+a+\sqrt{p^2+q^2-a^2}}{p+q+a-\sqrt{p^2+q^2-a^2}}$	$\frac{1}{\sqrt{x^2+y^2}} e^{-a\sqrt{x^2+y^2}}$
4.18	$\frac{pq}{\sqrt{p^2+q^2-a^2}} \times \ln \frac{pq-a\sqrt{p^2+q^2-a^2}}{pq+a\sqrt{p^2+q^2-a^2}}$	$\frac{2}{\sqrt{x^2+y^2}} \operatorname{sh}(a\sqrt{x^2+y^2})$
4.19	$\frac{pq}{\sqrt{p^2+q^2-a^2}} \times \ln \left\{ \frac{p^2+pq+q^2+(p+q) \times \sqrt{p^2+q^2-a^2}-a^2}{p^2+pq+q^2-(p+q) \times \sqrt{p^2+q^2-a^2}-a^2} \right\}$	$\frac{2}{\sqrt{x^2+y^2}} \operatorname{ch}(a\sqrt{x^2+y^2})$
4.20	$\frac{q}{\sqrt{p^2+q^2}} \ln \frac{p+q+\sqrt{p^2+q^2}}{p+q-\sqrt{p^2+q^2}}$	$\operatorname{arsh} \frac{x}{y}$
4.21	$\frac{q}{\ln pq}$	$x \int_0^\infty \frac{(xy)^{\xi-1}}{\Gamma(\xi)\Gamma(\xi+1)} d\xi$
4.22	$\frac{q}{p^{n-1} \ln pq}$	$x^n \int_0^\infty \frac{(xy)^{\xi-1}}{\Gamma(\xi)\Gamma(\xi+n)} d\xi$
4.23	$\frac{p}{p+\ln q}$	$\frac{y^x}{\Gamma(x+1)}$
4.24	$\frac{p}{q(p+\ln q)}$	$\frac{y^{x+1}}{\Gamma(x+2)}$

continued

№	$F(p, q)$	$f(x, y)$
4.25	$\frac{p}{q^n(p+\ln q)}$	$\frac{y^{x+n}}{\Gamma(x+n+1)}$
4.26	$\frac{pq}{(p+\ln q)^2}$	$\frac{xy^{x-1}}{\Gamma(x)}$
4.27	$\frac{p}{(p+\ln q)^2}$	$\frac{y^x}{\Gamma(x)}$
4.28	$\frac{p}{(p+\ln q)^{n+1}}$	$\frac{x^n y^x}{n!\,\Gamma(x+1)}$
4.29	$\frac{p}{q^n(p+\ln q)^{m+1}}$	$\frac{x^m y^{x+n}}{m!\,\Gamma(x+n+1)}$

HYPERBOLIC AND INVERSE HYPERBOLIC FUNCTIONS

№	$F(p, q)$	$f(x, y)$
5.1	$\frac{pq}{\sqrt{p^2+q^2}} \operatorname{arth} \frac{\sqrt{p^2+q^2}}{p+q}$	$\frac{1}{2\sqrt{x^2+y^2}}$
5.2	$\frac{pq}{\sqrt{p^2-q^2}} \operatorname{sh}\left(\nu \operatorname{arch} \frac{p}{q}\right)$ $\lvert \operatorname{Re} \nu \rvert < 1$	$\begin{cases} \frac{\sin \nu\pi}{\pi} \frac{\operatorname{ch}\left[\nu \operatorname{arch} \frac{y}{x}\right]}{\sqrt{y^2-x^2}} & \text{for } y > x, \\ 0 & \text{for } y < x \end{cases}$
5.3	$\frac{pq^{\frac{\nu}{2}+1}}{\sqrt{p^2-q}} \operatorname{sh}\left(\nu \operatorname{arch} \frac{p}{\sqrt{q}}\right)$ $\lvert \operatorname{Re} \nu \rvert < 1$	$\frac{\sin \nu\pi}{\pi} \frac{x^\nu e^{-\frac{x^2}{4y}}}{(2y)^{\nu+1}}$

continued

№	$F(p, q)$	$f(x, y)$
5.4	$\frac{pqe^{-(p+q)}}{(p-a)(p-q-a)} \times$ $\times \operatorname{sh}(p-q-a)$	$\begin{cases} \frac{1}{2} e^{a(x-1)} & \text{for } 2-x<y<2, \\ 0 & \text{otherwise} \end{cases}$
5.5	$\frac{qe^{-(p+q)}}{p-q+a} \operatorname{sh}(p-q+a)$	$\begin{cases} \frac{1}{2} e^{a(y-1)} & \text{for } 2-x<y<2, \\ 0 & \text{otherwise} \end{cases}$
5.6	$\sqrt{q} e^{-\sqrt{pq}} \operatorname{sh} \sqrt{pq}$	$\begin{cases} 0 & \text{for } y>\frac{1}{x}, \\ \frac{1}{2\sqrt{\pi y}} & \text{for } y<\frac{1}{x} \end{cases}$
5.7	$\frac{p\sqrt{q}}{p^2-q}\left[\frac{p}{\operatorname{sh}\sqrt{q}}-\frac{\sqrt{q}}{\operatorname{sh} p}\right]$	$\vartheta_0\left(\frac{x}{2}, y\right)=\vartheta_3\left(\frac{x+1}{2}\ y\right)$
5.8	$\frac{p^2q^2}{p+\operatorname{arsh} q}$ $\operatorname{Re}(p+\operatorname{arsh} q)>0$	$\begin{cases} \frac{x}{y} J_x(y) & \text{for } x>0,\ y>0, \\ 0 & \text{otherwise} \end{cases}$
5.9	$\frac{(p^2\sqrt{q}\operatorname{cth}\sqrt{q}-pq\operatorname{cth} p)\,pq}{p^2-q}$	$\begin{cases} Q_3\left(\frac{1}{2}x, \pi y\right) & \text{for } x>0,\ y>0, \\ 0 & \text{otherwise} \end{cases}$

CYLINDER FUNCTIONS

№	$F(p, q)$	$f(x, y)$
6.1	$\sqrt{pq} I_0\left(2\sqrt[4]{pq}\right)$	$\frac{1}{\sqrt{\pi xy}} I_0\left(\frac{1}{2\sqrt{xy}}\right)$
6.2	$\frac{\pi}{2} pq\,[H_0(\sqrt{pq})-Y_0(\sqrt{pq})]$	$\frac{1}{\pi\sqrt{xy}}\ \frac{1}{1+4xy}$

continued

№	$F(p, q)$	$f(x, y)$
6.3	$\frac{\pi}{2} q \left[H_1\left(\sqrt{\frac{q}{p}}\right) - Y_1\left(\sqrt{\frac{q}{p}}\right)\right] - q$	$\frac{1}{\pi y} K_1\left(\frac{x}{y}\right)$
6.4	$\sqrt{pq}\, J_0\left(\frac{1}{2\sqrt{pq}}\right)$	$\frac{1}{\pi\sqrt{xy}} \operatorname{ber}(2\sqrt[4]{xy})$
6.5	$\sqrt{\frac{q}{p}} K_1\left(\sqrt{\frac{q}{p}}\right)$	$J_0\left(\sqrt{\frac{x}{y}}\right)$
6.6	$\frac{\pi}{2}\frac{q}{p}\left[H_1\left(\frac{q}{p}\right) - Y_1\left(\frac{q}{p}\right) - \frac{2}{\pi}\right]$	$J_1\left(\frac{x}{y}\right)$
6.7	$\frac{\pi}{2} pq\, [H_0(pq) - Y_0(pq)]$	$J_0(xy)$
6.8	$\frac{p^{\frac{\nu}{2}+1}}{q^{\frac{\nu}{2}-1}} K_\nu(\sqrt{pq})$	$\begin{cases} \frac{1}{(2x)^{\nu+1}} & \text{for } y > \frac{1}{4x}, \\ 0 & \text{for } y < \frac{1}{4x} \end{cases}$
6.9	$4p^{k+\frac{1}{2}} q \cdot K_{2m}\left(\sqrt{2q\sqrt{p}e^{\frac{1}{4}\pi i}}\right) \times$ $\times K_{2m}\left(\sqrt{2q\sqrt{p}e^{-\frac{1}{4}\pi i}}\right)$	$x^{-k} e^{-\frac{1}{2xy^2}} W_{k,m}\left(\frac{1}{xy^2}\right)$
6.10	$4\sqrt{\pi p} \cdot q K_{2m}\left(\sqrt{2q\sqrt{p}e^{\frac{1}{4}\pi i}}\right) \times$ $\times K_{2m}\left(\sqrt{2q\sqrt{p}e^{-\frac{1}{4}\pi i}}\right)$	$\frac{e^{-\frac{1}{2xy^2}} K_m\left(\frac{1}{2xy^2}\right)}{y\sqrt{x}}$
6.11	$4p^{m+1} q K_{2m}\left(\sqrt{2q\sqrt{p}e^{\frac{1}{4}\pi i}}\right) \times$ $\times K_{2m}\left(\sqrt{2q\sqrt{p}e^{-\frac{1}{4}\pi i}}\right)$	$\frac{1}{x^{2m+1} y^{2m+1}} \cdot e^{-\frac{1}{xy^2}}$

continued

№	$F(p, q)$	$f(x, y)$
6.12	$4pqK_0\left(\sqrt{2q\sqrt{p}e^{\frac{1}{4}\pi i}}\right)\times$ $\times K_0\left(\sqrt{2q\sqrt{p}e^{-\frac{1}{4}\pi i}}\right)$	$\frac{1}{xy}e^{-\frac{1}{xy^2}}$
6.13	$4q\sqrt{p}K_1\left(\sqrt{2q\sqrt{p}e^{\frac{1}{4}\pi i}}\right)\times$ $\times K_1\left(\sqrt{2q\sqrt{p}e^{-\frac{1}{4}\pi i}}\right)$	$e^{-\frac{1}{xy^2}}$
6.14	$\frac{\sqrt{\pi}\Gamma\left(\frac{1}{2}-\mu\right)\Gamma(2\lambda+1)}{2^{\mu+1}}\times$ $\times q^{1+\mu}p^{\frac{1}{2}(1+\mu-4\lambda)}\times$ $\times[H_{-\mu}(q\sqrt{p})-Y_{-\mu}(q\sqrt{p})]$	$e^{-\frac{1}{2}xy^2}x^{\lambda-\frac{1}{2}}y^{-2\lambda-1}\times$ $\times M_{\mu-\lambda,\lambda}(xy^2)$
6.15	$\frac{\sqrt{\pi}\Gamma(-2m)\Gamma(1+2m)}{2^{2m+\frac{3}{2}}}\times$ $\times p^{\frac{1}{2}\left(\frac{3}{2}-2m\right)}q^{\frac{3}{2}+2m}\times$ $\times\left[H_{-2m-\frac{1}{2}}(q\sqrt{p})-\right.$ $\left.-Y_{-2m-\frac{1}{2}}(q\sqrt{p})\right]$ $-\frac{1}{2}<m<0$	$x^{2m}e^{-xy^2}$

INTEGRAL FUNCTIONS

№	$F(p, q)$	$f(x, y)$
7.1	$\frac{q}{p^{n-1}} S(n, pq),\ n > 0$	$\frac{1}{(n-1)!} \frac{P(xy, n)}{y^n}$
7.2	$\frac{q}{p^{\nu-2}} S(\nu, pq)$ $\operatorname{Re} \nu > 0$	$\frac{x^{\nu-1}}{\Gamma(\nu)} e^{-xy}$
7.3	$\frac{q}{p^{\mu-1}} S(\nu, pq)$ $\operatorname{Re} \nu > 0$ $\operatorname{Re} \mu > -1$	$\frac{y^{\frac{\mu-1}{2}} e^{-\frac{xy}{2}}}{(-1)^{\nu-\mu-1} \Gamma(\nu) x^{\frac{\mu+1}{2}}} \times$ $\times W_{\nu-\frac{\mu+1}{2}, \frac{\mu}{2}}(xy)$
7.4	$pq [\cos(2\sqrt{pq}) \operatorname{ci}(2\sqrt{pq}) +$ $+ \sin(2\sqrt{pq}) \operatorname{si}(2\sqrt{pq})]$	$-\frac{\pi}{8} \cdot \frac{1}{(1+xy)^{3/2}}$
7.5	$pqe^{p^2 q} \operatorname{Ei}(-p^2 q)$	$-\frac{\sin x\sqrt{y}}{\sqrt{y}}$
7.6	$p^2 qe^{p^2 q} \operatorname{Ei}(-p^2 q)$	$-\cos x\sqrt{y}$
7.7	$qe^{\frac{q}{p}} \operatorname{Ei}\left(-\frac{q}{p}\right)$	$-\frac{1}{y} e^{-\frac{x}{y}}$
7.8	$\frac{q}{p} e^{\frac{q}{p}} \operatorname{Ei}\left(-\frac{q}{p}\right)$	$e^{-\frac{x}{y}} - 1$
7.9	$pq [\sin(pq) \operatorname{ci}(pq) - \cos(pq) \operatorname{si}(pq)]$	$\cos xy$
7.10	$pq [\cos(p\sqrt{q}) \operatorname{ci}(p\sqrt{q}) +$ $+ \sin(p\sqrt{q}) \operatorname{si}(p\sqrt{q})]$	$-xe^{-x^2 y}$

continued

№	$F(p, q)$	$f(x, y)$
7.11	$p\sqrt{q}\,[\sin(p\sqrt{q})\,\mathrm{ci}(p\sqrt{q}) - \cos(p\sqrt{q})\,\mathrm{si}(p\sqrt{q})]$	$e^{-x^2 y}$
7.12	$\frac{2^{\nu+1}\Gamma\left(\nu+\frac{3}{2}\right)}{\sqrt{\pi}} \cdot \frac{q}{p^{2\nu-1}} S\left(\nu+\frac{3}{2}, p^2 q\right)$	$x^{\nu+1} y^{-\frac{\nu}{2}} J_\nu(x\sqrt{y})$
7.13	$\frac{2^{\nu}\Gamma\left(\nu+\frac{1}{2}\right)}{\sqrt{\pi}} \cdot \frac{q}{p^{2\nu-2}} \cdot S\left(\nu+\frac{1}{2}, p^2 q\right)$	$x^{\nu} y^{-\frac{\nu}{2}} J_\nu(x\sqrt{y})$
7.14	$\left(\frac{\beta}{p}\right)^{n-1} q\left[\sin\frac{pq+\alpha}{\beta}\,\mathrm{Ci}\left(\frac{pq+\alpha}{\beta}\right) - \cos\frac{pq+\alpha}{\beta}\,\mathrm{Si}\left(\frac{pq+\alpha}{\beta}\right)\right]$	$y^{-n} U_n(2\beta xy, 2\sqrt{\alpha xy})$
7.15	$e^{-pq}\,\mathrm{Ei}(pq) - \ln pq - C$	$\mathrm{Ei}(xy)$
7.16	$e^{-pq} pq\,\mathrm{Ei}(pq)$	e^{xy}
7.17	$pqe^{pq}\,\mathrm{Ei}(pq)$	e^{-xy}
7.18	$-pqe^{p^2 q}\,\mathrm{Ei}(-p^2 q)$	$\frac{\sin x\sqrt{x}}{\sqrt{y}}$
7.19	$4\pi\sqrt{pq}\,\mathrm{Ei}\left(-\sqrt{q\sqrt{p}}\right)$	$\frac{1}{\sqrt{xy}}\,\mathrm{Ei}\left(-\frac{1}{64xy^2}\right)$
7.20	$-p^2 qe^{p^2 q}\,\mathrm{Ei}(-p^2 q)$	$\cos(x\sqrt{y})$

continued

№	$F(p, q)$	$f(x, y)$
7.21	$K\left(\frac{1}{pq}\right)$	$\frac{1}{2}\frac{J_0(2\sqrt{xy})}{\sqrt{x}} \overset{x}{*} \frac{I_0(2\sqrt{xy})}{\sqrt{x}}$
7.22	$\frac{pq}{\sqrt{p^2q^2+1}} K\left(\frac{1}{\sqrt{p^2q^2+1}}\right)$	$\frac{1}{2}\frac{J_0(2\sqrt{ixy})}{\sqrt{x}} \overset{x}{*} \frac{I_0(2\sqrt{ixy})}{\sqrt{x}}$

CONFLUENT HYPERGEOMETRIC FUNCTIONS

№	$F(p, q)$	$f(x, y)$
8.1	$pqe^{p^2q}\operatorname{erfc}(p\sqrt{q})$	$\frac{\cos x\sqrt{y}}{\pi\sqrt{y}}$
8.2	$\frac{p\sqrt{q}}{\sqrt{\pi}} - p^2qe^{p^2q}\operatorname{erfc}(p\sqrt{q})$	$\frac{\sin x\sqrt{y}}{\pi}$
8.3	$qe^{p^2q}\operatorname{erfc}(p\sqrt{q})$	$\frac{\sin x\sqrt{y}}{\pi y}$
8.4	$\frac{p}{q}\cdot e^{\frac{p^2}{4q}} D_{-2}\left(\frac{p}{\sqrt{q}}\right)$	$\begin{cases} x & \text{for } y > \frac{x^2}{2}, \\ 0 & \text{for } y < \frac{x^2}{2} \end{cases}$
8.5	$e^{\frac{p}{2q}} W_{-1, \frac{1}{2}}\left(\frac{p}{q}\right)$	$e^{-\frac{y}{x}}$
8.6	$p\sqrt{q}e^{p^2q}\operatorname{erfc}(p\sqrt{q})$	$\frac{1}{\sqrt{\pi}} J_0(x\sqrt{y})$
8.7	$\sqrt{pq}e^{\frac{p}{q}}\operatorname{erfc}\left(\sqrt{\frac{p}{q}}\right)$	$\frac{1}{\pi\sqrt{xy}} e^{-\frac{y}{x}}$

continued

№	$F(p, q)$	$f(x, y)$
8.8	$\sqrt{p}\, e^{\frac{q^2}{p}} \operatorname{erfc}\left(\frac{q}{\sqrt{p}}\right)$	$\begin{cases} \frac{1}{\sqrt{\pi x}} & \text{for} \quad y > 2\sqrt{x}, \\ 0 & \text{for} \quad y < 2\sqrt{x} \end{cases}$
8.9	$\frac{p}{\sqrt{q}} e^{\frac{p^2}{q}} \operatorname{erfc}\left(\frac{p}{\sqrt{q}}\right)$	$\begin{cases} \frac{1}{\sqrt{\pi}} & \text{for} \quad y > \frac{x^2}{4}, \\ 0 & \text{for} \quad y < \frac{x^2}{4} \end{cases}$
8.10	$\frac{p}{q\sqrt{q}} e^{\frac{p^2}{q}} \operatorname{erfc}\left(\frac{p}{\sqrt{q}}\right)$	$\begin{cases} \frac{1}{\sqrt{\pi}}\left(y - \frac{x^2}{4}\right) & \text{for} \quad y > \frac{x^2}{4}, \\ 0 & \text{for} \quad y < \frac{x^2}{4} \end{cases}$
8.11	$\frac{p}{q^{\frac{\nu}{2}}} e^{\frac{p^2}{4q}} D_{-\nu}\left(\frac{p}{\sqrt{q}}\right)$ $\operatorname{Re} \nu > 0$	$\begin{cases} \frac{x^{\nu-1}}{\Gamma(\nu)} & \text{for} \quad y > \frac{x^2}{2}, \\ 0 & \text{for} \quad y < \frac{x^2}{2} \end{cases}$
8.12	$\frac{1}{(pq)^{\chi-1}} e^{-\frac{1}{2pq}} M_{\chi, \mu}\left(\frac{1}{pq}\right)$ $\operatorname{Re}(\chi + \mu) > -\frac{1}{2}$	$\frac{\Gamma(2\mu + 1)}{\Gamma\left(\chi + \mu + \frac{1}{2}\right)} (xy)^{\frac{2\chi-1}{3}} \times$ $\times J_{\chi+\mu-\frac{1}{2},\, 2\mu}\left(3\sqrt[3]{xy}\right)$
8.13	$\frac{\sqrt{\pi}\,\Gamma\left(m + \frac{1}{2}\right)}{2^{\frac{1}{2}\left(n+\frac{1}{2}\right)}} p^{\frac{1}{4}(m-n+1)} \times$ $\times q^{\frac{1}{2}(n-m+1)} e^{\frac{1}{2} q\sqrt{p}} \times$ $\times W_{-\frac{1}{2}(n+m), -\frac{1}{2}(n-m)}(q\sqrt{p})$ $\operatorname{Re}(n - m) > -3$	$x^{\frac{1}{2}\left(n-\frac{1}{2}\right)} y^{m-\frac{1}{2}} e^{\frac{1}{2}xy^2} \times$ $\times D_{-n-\frac{1}{2}}(y\sqrt{2x})$

continued

№	$F(p, q)$	$f(x, y)$
8.14	$q\sqrt{p}D_{-n-1}\left(\frac{1}{2}q\sqrt{p}\right)\times D_{-n-1}\left(-\frac{1}{2}q\sqrt{p}\right)$	$\frac{(-1)^n 2\sqrt{\pi}}{\Gamma(n+1)}\times\left[\mathrm{ber}^2_{n+\frac{1}{2}}(2y\sqrt{x})+\mathrm{bei}^2_{n+\frac{1}{2}}(2y\sqrt{x})\right]$
8.15	$\pi^{-\frac{1}{2}}\Gamma\left(m+\frac{1}{2}\right)q\sqrt{p}\times D_{-m-\frac{1}{2}}\left(q\sqrt{p}e^{\frac{1}{4}\pi i}\right)\times D_{-m-\frac{1}{2}}\left(q\sqrt{p}e^{-\frac{1}{4}\pi i}\right)$	$J_m(y\sqrt{x})I_m(y\sqrt{x})$
8.16	$\pi p^{\frac{1}{4}}qe^{q\sqrt{p}}\left[1-\mathrm{erf}\sqrt{q\sqrt{p}}\right]$	$y^{-\frac{1}{2}}e^{xy^2}[1-\mathrm{erf}(y\sqrt{x})]$
8.17	$\sqrt{\pi}\frac{(-1)^m}{p^{4m}q^{m-\frac{1}{2}}}\times e^{-\frac{1}{4p^2q}}D_{2m}\left(\frac{1}{p\sqrt{q}}\right)$	$x^{2m}y^{-\frac{1}{2}}\mathrm{ber}_{4m}\left(2\sqrt{x\sqrt{2y}}\right)$
8.18	$\frac{(-1)^m\sqrt{\pi}}{2^{m-\frac{\nu}{2}}}\frac{1}{p^{2\nu}q^{m-\frac{1}{2}}}e^{-\frac{1}{4p^2q}}\times D_{2m}\left(\frac{1}{p\sqrt{q}}\right)$	$x^{\nu}y^{m-\frac{1}{2}\nu-\frac{1}{2}}\times\left[\mathrm{ber}_{2\nu}\left(2\sqrt{x\sqrt{2y}}\right)\cos\frac{3\nu\pi}{2}+\mathrm{bei}_{2\nu}\left(2\sqrt{x\sqrt{2y}}\right)\sin\frac{3\nu\pi}{2}\right]$

continued

№	$F(p, q)$	$f(x, y)$
8.19	$\sqrt{\frac{\pi}{2}\frac{(-1)^m}{p^{4m}q^m}}\, e^{-\frac{1}{4p^2q}} \times D_{2m+1}\left(\frac{1}{p\sqrt{q}}\right)$	$x^{2m}\,\mathrm{bei}_{4m}\left(2\sqrt{x\sqrt{2y}}\right)$
8.20	$\frac{(-1)^m\sqrt{\pi}}{2^{m-\frac{\nu}{2}+\frac{1}{2}}}\cdot\frac{1}{p^{2\nu}q^m}\times e^{-\frac{1}{4p^2q}}\cdot D_{2m+1}\left(\frac{1}{p\sqrt{q}}\right)$	$x^{\nu}y^{m-\frac{\nu}{2}}\left[\mathrm{bei}_{2m}\left(2\sqrt{x\sqrt{2y}}\right)\times\cos\frac{3\nu\pi}{2} - \mathrm{ber}\left(2\sqrt{x\sqrt{2y}}\right)\sin\frac{3\nu\pi}{2}\right]$
8.21	$\frac{(-1)^m}{2^{\frac{1}{3}(3m+k+1)}}\cdot\frac{1}{p^kq^m}e^{-\frac{1}{4pq}}\times D_{2m+1}\left(\frac{1}{\sqrt{pq}}\right)$	$x^{\frac{1}{6}(4k+1)}y^{\frac{1}{6}(6m-2k+1)}\times J_{\frac{1}{2}(2k+1),\,\frac{1}{2}}\left(3\sqrt[3]{\frac{1}{2}xy}\right)$
8.22	$\frac{(-1)^m}{2^{\frac{1}{6}(6m+2k-1)}}\cdot\frac{1}{p^kq^{m-\frac{1}{2}}}\times e^{-\frac{1}{4pq}}\cdot D_{2m}\left(\frac{1}{\sqrt{pq}}\right)$	$x^{\frac{1}{6}(4k+1)}y^{\frac{1}{6}(6m-2k-2)}\times J_{k,\,-\frac{1}{2}}\left(3\sqrt[3]{\frac{1}{2}xy}\right)$
8.23	$\Gamma(1+n-\mu)\,\Gamma(2n)\,p^{1-n}\times q^{\mu}e^{\frac{1}{2}pq}W_{-n,\,-\mu+\frac{1}{2}}(pq)$	$x^{n-1}y^{-\mu}M_{\mu,\,n-\frac{1}{2}}(xy)\,e^{-\frac{1}{2}xy}$
8.24	$\frac{1}{\sqrt{2}}pqe^{\frac{1}{4}p^2q^2}D_{-\frac{3}{2}}(pq)$	$(xy)^{\frac{1}{2}}J_{-\frac{1}{4},\,\frac{1}{4}}\left[3\sqrt[3]{\frac{1}{8}x^2y^2}\right]$

continued

№	$F(p, q)$	$f(x, y)$
8.25	$\sqrt{\frac{2}{\pi}}\, q \sqrt{p}\, e^{\frac{1}{4} p^2q^2} D_{-1}(pq)$	$x^{\frac{1}{2}} J_{-\frac{1}{4}, \frac{1}{4}}\left[3 \sqrt[3]{\frac{1}{8} x^2y^2}\right]$
8.26	$\sqrt{\frac{2}{\pi}}\, \Gamma(m+1) \times$ $\times\, pqe^{\frac{1}{4} p^2q^2} D_{-(m+1)}(pq)$	$(xy)^{\frac{1}{3}(m+1)} \times$ $\times\, J_{\frac{1}{2}(m-1), \frac{1}{2} m}\left[3 \sqrt[3]{\frac{x^2y^2}{8}}\right]$
8.27	$\sqrt{\frac{2}{\pi}}\, \Gamma(m+k) \times$ $\times\, qp^k e^{\frac{1}{4} p^2q^2} D_{-(m+k)}(pq)$	$x^{\frac{1}{3}(m+1)} y^{\frac{1}{3}(m+3k-2)} \times$ $\times\, J_{\frac{1}{2}(m-1), \frac{1}{2} m}\left[3 \sqrt[3]{\frac{1}{8} x^2y^2}\right]$
8.28	$\sqrt{\frac{\pi}{2}}\, \Gamma(k+1) \times$ $\times\, qp^{\frac{1}{2} k} e^{\frac{1}{4} pq^2} D_{-(k+1)}(q\sqrt{p})$	$y^{k-1} \sin(y\sqrt{2x})$
8.29	$\sqrt{\pi p}\, qe^{\frac{1}{2} pq^2} D_{-2}(q\sqrt{2p})$	$\sin(y\sqrt{x})$
8.30	$q\sqrt{p}\, e^{\frac{1}{4} pq^2} D_{-1}(q\sqrt{p})$	$J_0(y\sqrt{2x})$
8.31	$\frac{\Gamma(2m+1)}{2^{\frac{1}{2} m}} q\sqrt{p}\, e^{\frac{1}{4} pq^2} \times$ $\times\, D_{-(2m+1)}(q\sqrt{p})$	$x^{\frac{1}{2} m} y^m J_m(y\sqrt{2x})$
8.32	$2^{-\frac{1}{2}} qe^{\frac{1}{4} pq^2} D_{-2}(q\sqrt{p})$	$x^{\frac{1}{2}} J_1(y\sqrt{2x})$

continued

№	$F(p, q)$	$f(x, y)$
8.33	$\dfrac{\Gamma(2m)}{2^{\frac{1}{2}m}} q e^{\frac{1}{4}pq^2} D_{-2m}(q\sqrt{p})$	$x^{\frac{1}{2}m} y^{m-1} J_m(y\sqrt{2x})$
8.34	$\dfrac{\Gamma(2m+k)}{2^{\frac{1}{2}m}} q p^{\frac{1}{2}k} e^{\frac{1}{4}pq^2} \times$ $\times D_{-(2m+k)}(q\sqrt{p})$	$x^{\frac{1}{2}m} y^{m+k-1} J_m(y\sqrt{2x})$
8.35	$\Gamma(n+k-1)\, q p^{\frac{mk}{n-1}} e^{\frac{1}{4}q^2 p^{\frac{2m}{n-1}}} \times$ $\times D_{-(n+k-1)}\left(q p^{\frac{m}{n-1}}\right)$	$x^m y^{n+k-2} J_m^{\frac{2m}{n-1}}\left(\frac{1}{2} y^2 x^{\frac{2m}{n-1}}\right)$
8.36	$\Gamma(\nu)\, p^{\mu(1+\nu)-\lambda} q e^{\frac{1}{4}p^{2\mu}q^2} \times$ $\times D_{-\nu}(p^{\mu} q)$	$x^{\lambda-\mu} y^{\nu-1} J_{\lambda-\mu}^{2\mu}\left(\frac{1}{2} y^2 x^{2\mu}\right)$
8.37	$\dfrac{1}{q^{b-c} p^a} \times$ $\times {}_2F_1\left(c, a+1; a+b+2; \dfrac{p-q}{p}\right)$ $a > -1,\ b > -1,\ c < a+b+2$	$\dfrac{\Gamma(a+b+2) \times}{\Gamma(a+1)\Gamma(b+1)\Gamma(a+b+2-c)}$ $\times \dfrac{x^a y^b}{(x+y)^c}$
8.38	${}_mF_n\left(a_1, \ldots, a_m; b_1, \ldots, b_n; \dfrac{1}{pq}\right)$ $n \geqslant m-3$	${}_mF_{n+2}(a_1, \ldots, a_m;$ $b_1, \ldots, b_n, 1, 1; xy)$
8.39	$\sqrt{pq}\, {}_0F_1(1, \sqrt{pq})$	$\dfrac{1}{\sqrt{\pi xy}}\, {}_0F_1\left(1; \dfrac{1}{16xy}\right)$

MISCELLANEOUS FUNCTIONS

№	$F(p, q)$	$f(x, y)$
9.1	$q\sqrt{p}Q_\nu(pq)$ $\operatorname{Re}\nu > -1$	$\sqrt{\frac{\pi}{2y}}J_{\nu+\frac{1}{2}}(\sqrt{2ixy})\times$ $\times J_{\nu+\frac{1}{2}}(\sqrt{-2ixy})$
9.2	$p^\nu q e^{pq} Q(pq, 1-\nu)$ $\operatorname{Re}\nu > 0$	$\frac{y^{\nu-1}}{\Gamma(\nu)}e^{-xy}$
9.3	$pqe^{(p+1)(q+1)}\times$ $\times \operatorname{Ei}\{(p+1)(q+1)\}$	$e^{-xy-x-y}$
9.4	$\frac{p}{q^{\mu-1}}P_\nu\left(\frac{p}{q}\right)$ $-1 < \operatorname{Re}\nu < 0$	$\begin{cases} -\frac{\sin\nu\pi}{\pi}\frac{(y^2-x^2)^{\frac{\mu-1}{2}}}{x}P_\nu^{1-\mu}\left(\frac{y}{x}\right) & \text{for } y > x, \\ 0 & \text{for } y < x \end{cases}$
9.5	$\frac{pq}{\sqrt{p^2q^2+1}}B\left(\frac{1}{\sqrt{p^2q^2+1}}\right)$	$\frac{1}{4}\frac{J_0(2\sqrt{ixy})}{\sqrt{x}}\overset{x}{*}\frac{I_0(2\sqrt{ixy})}{\sqrt{x}}+$ $+\frac{1}{4}\frac{J_2(2\sqrt{ixy})}{\sqrt{x}}\overset{x}{*}\frac{I_2(2\sqrt{ixy})}{\sqrt{x}}$
9.6	$\frac{pq}{(p^2q^2+1)^{3/2}}\times$ $\times C\left(\frac{1}{\sqrt{p^2q^2+1}}\right)$	$-\frac{1}{2}\frac{J_2(2\sqrt{ixy})}{\sqrt{x}}\overset{x}{*}\frac{I_2(2\sqrt{ixy})}{\sqrt{x}}$
9.7	$\frac{pq}{\sqrt{p^2q^2+1}}\times$ $\times D\left(\frac{1}{\sqrt{p^2q^2+1}}\right)$	$\frac{1}{4}\frac{J_0(2\sqrt{ixy})}{\sqrt{x}}\overset{x}{*}\frac{I_0(2\sqrt{ixy})}{\sqrt{x}}-$ $-\frac{1}{4}\frac{J_2(2\sqrt{ixy})}{\sqrt{x}}\overset{x}{*}\frac{I_2(2\sqrt{ixy})}{\sqrt{x}}$

continued

№	$F(p, q)$	$f(x, y)$
9.8	$\lambda(qe^p, a)$	$\begin{cases} \dfrac{y^x - y^a}{\ln y} & \text{for } x > a > 0 \\ 0 & \text{for } x < a \end{cases}$
9.9	$\nu\left(\dfrac{e^{-p}}{q}\right)$	$\int_0^x \dfrac{y^s\,ds}{[\Gamma(1+s)]^2}$
9.10	$\int_0^\alpha \dfrac{\Gamma^2(s+1)}{(pq)^s}\,ds$	$\dfrac{(xy)^\alpha - 1}{\ln xy}$

REFERENCES

1. B. VAN-DER POL and H.BREMMER. Operational Calculus based on the two-sided Laplace integral; Cambridge University Press, 1950.

2. V.A.DITKIN and P.I.KUZNETSOV. Manual of Operational Calculus (Spravochnik po operatsionnomy ischisleniyu), Gostekhizdat, 1951.

3. M.A.LAVRENT'YEV and B.V.SHABOT. Methods of the theory of a complex variable (Metody teorii kompleksnogo peremennogo), Chapter VI, Fizmatgiz, 1958.

4. A.V.LYKOV. Theory of heat conduction (Teoriya teploprovodnosti), Gostekhizdat, Moscow 1952.

5. A.V.LYKOV. Heat and mass exchange in drying processes (Teplo i massoobmen v protsessakh sushki), Gosenergoizdat, Moscow-Leningrad, 1956.

6. JAN MIKUSINSKII. Operational Calculus. English translation published by Pergamon Press, 1960.

7. A.N.LUR'YE. Operational Calculus (Operatsionnoye ischisleniye), Gostekhizdat, 1950.

8. L.AMERIO. Sulla trasformata doppia di Laplace. Atti Accad. Italia Mem. Cl. Sci. Fis. Mat.natur. 12 (1941), 707-780.

9. D.L.BERNSTEIN. The double Laplace integral, Duke Math. Journ. 8 (1941), 460-496.

10. S.K.BOSE. Generalized Laplace integral of two variables, Ganita 3 (1952), 23-35.

11. N.K.CHAKRABARTY. Sur le calcul symbolique à deux variables. Ann. Soc. Sci., Bruxelles, 67 (1953), 23-28, 203-218.

12. N.K.CHAKRABARTY. On some theorems and inequalities in operational calculus with two variables. Bull. Calcutta Math. Soc. 46 (1954), No.4, 221-235.

13. N.K.CHAKRABARTY. On symbolic calculus of two variables, Acta Mathematica, 93 (1955) 1-14.

14. G.A.COON and D.L.BERNSTEIN. Some properties of the double Laplace transformation. Trans. Amer. Math. Soc. 74, (1953), No.1, 135-176.

15. CHENG MIN-TEH. On a theorem of Nicolesco and generalized Laplace operators. Proc. Amer. Math. Soc.2 (1951), 77-86.

16. R.V.CHURCHILL. Modern operational mathematics in engineering. New York and London, 1944, 210-214.

17. H.DELAVAULT. Sur un problème de la théorie de la chaleur et sa solution au moyen de la transformation de Hankel, Comptes Rendus Acad. Sci., 237 (1953), 2484-2485.

18. H.DELAVAULT. Sur un problème de la théorie de la chaleur et sa solution au moyen des transformations de Fourier et de Laplace, Comptes Rendus Acad. Sci., 237 (1953), 1067-1068.

19. P.DELERUE. Sur le calcul symbolique à n variables et sur les fonctions hyperbesseliennes., Ann. Soc. Sci. Bruxelles, 67 (1953), 83-105, 229-275.

20. P.DELERUE. Sur quelques images en calcul symbolique à 3 et n variables. Bull. Sci. Math. 1952.

21. P.DELERUE. Le calcul symbolique à 2 ou n variables et équations integrales. Ann. Soc. Sci. Bruxelles, Oct. 1956, p.96.

22. G.DOETSCH. L application de la transformation bi-dimensionalle de Laplace dans la théorie des équations aux dérivées partielles. Premier colloque sur les équations aux dérivées partielles, Paris, 1954, 63-78.

23. A.y VEDIA DURANONA and C.A.TREJO. Recintos de convergencia de las integrales dobles de Laplace - Stieltjes. Universidad Nacional La Plata, Publ. Fac. Ci. fis.-mat., 1 (1936), 315-327.

24. A.y VEDIA DURANONA and C.A.TREJO. Uber die Umkehrung des Laplace - Stieltjesschen doppelintegrals. Universidad Nacional La Plata, Publ. Fac. Ci. fis.-mat., 1 (1938), 451-464.

25. A.ERDELYI. Untersuchungen über Produkte von Whittakerschen Funktionen. Monatshefte Math. Phys., 46 (1937), 132-156.

26. A.ERDELYI. Beitrag zur Theorie der konfluenten hypergeometrischen Funktionen von mehreren Veränderlichen. Sitz. Ber. Akad. Wiss. Wien, math-nat. Kl. 2-a, 146 (1937),431-467.

27. S.FAEDO. Sulle trasformate multiple di Laplace. Atti. Accad. Italia, Rend. Cl. Sci. fiz. mat. natur. (7), 2 (1941), 722-727.

28. J.GILLY. Les parties finies d'integrals et la transformation de Laplace-Carson, Revue Scientifique 83 (1945), 259-270.

29. G.GIORGI. Metodi moderni di Calcolo operatorio funzionale, Rend. del Sem. Mat. 8, Milan, 1934, 189-214.

30. E.K.HAVILAND. On the inversion formula for Fourier-Stieltjes transforms in more than one dimension. Amer. J. Math. 57 (1935), 382-388.

31. A.E.HEINS. Note on the equation of heat conduction. Bull. Amer. Math. Soc., 41, 253-258.

32. A.E.HEINS. Applications of the Fourier transform theorem. J. Math. Massachusetts, 14, 137-142.

33. P.HUMBERT. Le calcul symbolique à deux variables. Comptes Rendus Acad. Sci., Paris, 199 (1934), 657-660.

34. P.HUMBERT, McLACHLAN et L.POLI. Supplément au formulaire. Mem. Sci. Math. Fasc., 113, Paris.

35. P.HUMBERT. Le calcul symbolique à deux variables. Ann. Soc. Sci. Bruxelles, A 56 (1936), 26-43.

36. J.C.JAEGER. The solution of boundary value problems by a double Laplace transformation. Bull. Amer. Math. Soc. 46 (1940), 687-693.

37. L.KOSCHMIEDER. Operationenrechnung in zwei Veränderlichen und bilineare Formel der Laguerreschen Polynome. Sitz. Ber. Akad. Wiss., Wien, math-nat. Kl. IIa, 145 (1936), 651-655.

38. W.KÜSTERMANN. Ueber Fouriesche Doppelreihen und des Poissonsche Doppelintegral, Inaugural-Dissertation, München, 1913, 1-61.

39. McLACHLAN and P.HUMBERT. Formulaire pour le calcul symbolique. Mem. Sci. math. Fasc., 100, Paris, 1947, p 67.

40. P.S.LAPLACE. Théorie analytiques des probabilités. Paris, 1812.

41. M.PICONE. Nuovi metcdi risolutivi per i problemi d'integrazione delle equazioni lineari a derivate parziali e nuova applicazione della trasformata multipla di Laplace nel caso delle equazioni a coefficienti costanti. Atti. Accad. Sci. Torino, 75 (1940), 1-14.

42. A.PISTOIA. Alcuni teoremi tauberiani per la trasformata doppia di Laplace. Istituto Lombardo di Scienze e Lettre. Rendiconti. Cl. Sci. Matem. e Natur. (3), 16 (85) (1952), 170-190.

43. A.PISTOIA. Sulla operazione di composizione secondo una varieta lineare per la trasformata multipla di Laplace. 1st. Lombardo Sci. Lett., Rend. Cl. Sci. mat. natur. 84 (1951), 241-249.

44. M.PLANCHEREL. Note sur les transformations linéares et les transformations de Fourier des fonctions de plusieurs variables. Comment. math. helv. 9 (1937), 249-262.

45. M.PLANCHEREL et G.POLYA. Fonctions entières et intégrales de Fourier multiples. Comment. math. helv. 9 (1937), 224-248.

46. M.PLANCHEREL et G.POLYA. Fonctions entières et intégrales de Fourier multiples. Comment. math. helv.10 (1937), 110-163.

47. M.PLANCHEREL. Quelques remarques sur les transformations de Fourier des fonctions de plusieurs variables. Vierteljschr. Naturforsch. Ges. Zurich 85 (1940), 20-26.

48. L.POLI. Le calcul symbolique à deux variables. Revue Scientifique. 85 (1947), 616-617.

49. L.POLI et P.DELERUE. Le calcul symbolique à deux variables et ses applications. Mem. Sci. Math. f. 127, (1954), p.77.

50. L.POLI. Calcul symbolique et équations aux derivées partielles. Cahiers Rhodaniens. 4 (1952), 13-27.

51. B.VAN DER POL and K.F.NIESSEN. On simultaneous operational calculus. Phil. Mag. 11 (1931), 368-376.

52. J.S.REED. The Mellin type of double integral. Duke Math. J. 11, (1944), 565-572.

53. U.RUELL. L'integrale di Fourier per funzioni di piu variabili. Istituto Elettrotec. Accad. Navale, Livorno, No.157 (1940) p.47.

54. L.SCHWARTZ. Théorie des distributions. Paris (1951).

55. H.M.SRIVASTAVA. On some sequences of Laplace transforms. Ann. Soc. Sci. Bruxelles, 67 (1953), 218-229.

56. S.VASILACHE. Asupra existentei unei solutii a ecuatiei integrali definite prin transformata lui Laplace cu doua variabile independente. Acad. Republ. Popul., Romane, Bul. Sti., Sect. Mat. Fiz. 3 (1951), 209-217.

57. S.VASILACHE. Asupra catorva formule fundamentale ale transformatei lui Laplace cu doua variabile. Acad. Republ., Popular. Romane, Bull. Sti., Sect. Mat. Fiz. 3 (1951), 429-432.

58. S.VASILACHE. Asupra catorva din teoria transformatei lui Laplace cu doua variabile. Comun. Acad. Repub. Pop. Romane, 2 (1952), 193-198.

59. J.C.VIGNAUX. Sobre la transformata de Abel-Laplace de dos variables. Ann. Soc. Sient. Arg., 116 (1932), 76-78.

60. J.C.VIGNAUX. Un teorema sulle integrali doppi di Abel-Laplace. Rend R. Accad. Naz, dei Lincei, (6), 17 (1933), 1055-1059.

61. J.C.VIGNAUX. Sur l'extension du théorème de Dirichlet aux intégrales doubles convergentes. Bull. Soc. R. Sci. Liège, 2 (1933), 109-112.

62. D.VOELKER und G.DÖETSCH. Die Zweidimensionale Laplace-Transformation. Basel, 1950.